Contents

Foreword

Element 1   **The foundations of health and safety leadership**   **5**

1.1   **Reasons for health and safety leadership, organisational health and safety vision and benefits of excellent health and safety leadership**   **6**
- What is health and safety leadership?   6
- The reasons for, and benefits of, effective health and safety leadership   7
- Behaviours/traits of a good health and safety leader   9
- Developing an agreed health and safety vision for an organisation (health and safety leadership value 1)   9
- The characteristics that make a good health and safety leader   11

1.2   **The moral, legal and financial reasons for good health and safety leadership**   **12**
- Moral   12
- Legal   14
- Content for UK students   15
- Content for international students   25
- Financial   26

1.3   **How leaders can gain assurance that health and safety is being managed effectively**   **28**
- Context of the organisation   28
- Risk profiling   28
- Management system thinking   28
- Leadership team involved, informed and visible   31
- Governance, competency and resource   31
- Approval and monitoring of performance indices   31
- Horizon scanning   32
- Benchmarking of organisational health and safety performance   32

1.4   **How good leadership can positively influence health and safety culture**   **34**
- The meaning of safety culture   34
- Promoting fairness and trust in relationships with others (health and safety leadership value 4)   36
- Environmental, health and safety (EHS) and management as a conduit for change   37
- Blame culture, no name no blame and just culture   37
- Three-aspect approach to health and safety culture   39
- Levels of maturity in health and safety culture   40
- Leading and lagging indicators of health and safety culture   42
- Measuring the 'right' things   43
- High Reliability Organisations (HROs)   46

Element 1 references / further reading   49

Element 2		Human failure and decision making	51
	2.1	**Understanding how human failure can impact on health and safety culture and how the 'Make it Happen' model can help to change behaviours**	**52**
		Errors	53
		Mistakes	54
		Violations	54
		The HSE's 'Make it Happen' model	56
		Providing support and recognition (health and safety leadership value 3)	58
	2.2	**Decision-making processes, mental shortcuts, perception biases and habits**	**59**
		The differences between 'Automatic' and 'Reflective' decision making	59
		Reliable mental shortcuts	61
		Common perception biases and how they affect decision making	67
		Habits and decision making	74
		Personal beliefs and how this can affect decision making	75
		Element 2 references / further reading	77
Element 3		Leadership	79
	3.1	**Different leadership styles**	**80**
		The transformational leader	80
		Transactional leadership	82
		Authentic leadership	84
		Resonant leadership	86
	3.2	**The supporting foundations of the leadership values**	**89**
		Involvement and communication	90
		Effective role modelling	90
		Embedding	90
		Being considerate and responsive (health and safety leadership value 2)	91
		Assessing own health and safety leadership performance	92
	3.3	**Building relationships with the workforce**	**93**
		Leadership walkabouts and rapport	93
		Barriers to building a good rapport with the workforce	97
		What good communication looks like	98
		Vroom's Model of Motivation	101
		How information can be given	102
		How to gather information	104
		Encouraging improvement, innovation and learning (health and safety leadership value 5)	106
		Positive reinforcement, negative reinforcement and punishment	107
		Element 3 references / further reading	111

Foreword

Health and safety is a key performance measure within successful and forward-thinking organisations. Effective leaders understand that health and safety is not just a moral imperative, but also contributes to the achievement of objectives across the organisational spectrum covering finance, operations, compliance and governance.

Productivity improvements, competitive advantage, talent retention and effective risk management are just a few of the things which flow from strong organisational health and safety performance and culture.

Whether it is finance, marketing, human resources, or health and safety, leaders should always seek to develop their high-level understanding within each component part of their organisation in order to monitor and positively influence overall performance. The NEBOSH HSE Certificate in Health and Safety Leadership Excellence is designed to support both leaders and aspiring leaders in gaining core understanding of how their behaviours and responsibilities directly impact on health and safety management.

This qualification, which combines NEBOSH's ability to deliver strong, credible vocational OSH qualifications with HSE's industry-leading knowledge and expertise, will enable you to set a clear and credible benchmark that your leadership peers will aspire to.

A guide to the symbols used in this course book

ACTIVITY
Carry out an activity to reinforce what you have just learned.

EXAMPLE
Real or imagined scenarios that give context to points made in the text

KEY TERMS
Definitions of key terminology

ASSESSMENT ACTIVITY
This symbol indicates that part of the assessment is to be undertaken. This must be done individually and not as part of a group activity. The accredited course provider will advise on the time to be allocated for each part of the assessment.

The HSE's five leadership values

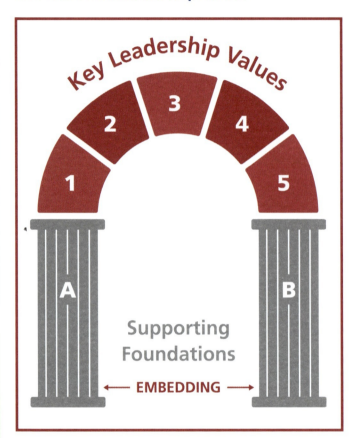

1. Building and promoting a shared H&S vision
2. Being considered and responsive
3. Providing support and recognition
4. Promoting fairness and trust in relationships with others
5. Encouraging improvement, innovation and learning

A. Involvement / communication
B. Effective role modelling

Wherever you see this diagram it indicates that one of the five leadership values will be discussed and assessed.

The foundations of health and safety leadership

This chapter will explore the reasons for good health and safety leadership, why a health and safety vision is important to an organisation and the benefits that good health and safety leadership can bring to an organisation. To further highlight these areas we will then look at the specific moral, legal and financial arguments for good health and safety leadership. Here we will be looking at the level of penalties that organisations and individuals can expect to see should health and safety legislation be breached. The chapter will conclude with a look at how leaders can gain assurance that their organisation is managing health and safety well and finally, the impact of good health and safety leadership on organisational health and safety culture.

Learning outcomes

- The reasons for health and safety leadership excellence, the importance of an agreed health and safety vision and the business benefits excellent health and safety leadership brings

- The moral, legal and financial reasons for good health and safety leadership

- How leaders can gain assurance that health and safety is being managed effectively

- How good leadership can positively influence health and safety culture.

Reasons for health and safety leadership, organisational health and safety vision and benefits of excellent health and safety leadership

Leadership actions

What is health and safety leadership?

> **KEY TERMS**
>
> **Leadership** can be defined as the capacity to influence people, by means of personal attributes and/or behaviours, to achieve a common goal. CIPD [1]

A debate has long existed about the differences between 'Management' and 'Leadership' across a wider spectrum than health and safety; sometimes it is difficult to determine what these differences might be. However, in the area of health and safety we can draw some clear distinctions about these terms.

It is perfectly possible, and hopefully probable, that a health and safety manager will also be a leader in health and safety. However, this does not mean that a health and safety leader automatically 'manages' the day-to-day functions of organisational health and safety or has ultimate responsibility for them.

When we start to examine the different styles of leadership it will become clear that leadership can come from many places and is not exclusively a 'top down' process. It can be, of course, but leadership is mainly about the ability to 'take people with you' and this skill can be present at all levels. It is, therefore, important that a good health and safety leader will not only have the necessary technical knowledge and skills, but that they also have 'soft skills' such as an open approachable personality, emotional intelligence, empathy etc.

Effective health and safety performance comes from the top; members of the board have both collective and individual responsibility for health and safety. Leaders need to examine their own behaviours, both individually and collectively and, where they see that they fall short, to change what they do to become more effective leaders in health and safety.

Why leaders need to act:

- protecting the health and safety of workers or members of the public who may be affected by workplace activities is an essential part of risk management and must be led by senior leaders/boards;

- failure to include health and safety as a key business risk in board decisions can have catastrophic results. Many high-profile safety cases over the years have been rooted in failures of leadership; and

- health and safety law places duties on organisations and employers, and directors can be personally liable when these duties are breached: members of the board have both collective and individual responsibility for health and safety.[2]

The reasons for, and benefits of, effective health and safety leadership

These should be self-evident in any organisation; however, it is unfortunately not always the case. *"The sad but true fact is that many organisations only get to learn the true cost of poor health and safety after an incident has occurred. Many high-profile incidents, trace their root causes back to failures of leadership at the very top and many result not just in high penalties, but cause the business to collapse due to irreparable reputation damage."* Dame Judith Hackitt, the past Chair of HSE.

If you do not regulate yourselves things are likely to go wrong; this is when you are going to meet the regulator. Investors want to know that they are investing in a well led/run organisation that performs well. In this day and age, your customers will expect you to evidence your good health and safety performance; there are many companies that will not include organisations in their supply chain who cannot evidence good health and safety management.

It is important for you to realise that an organisation's reputation is built over many years but it can be destroyed in seconds. Any adverse incidents will have a major impact on all stakeholder interactions which include productivity, investment, sales and regulatory action.

Even if health and safety law did not exist, there are still sound business drivers that makes investing in good health and safety good business sense. If health and safety is not managed well by its leaders, and things do go wrong, this will have a massive effect on the organisation. As well as the financial reasons, which we will discuss in more detail later, it could mean that the business is totally destroyed; this will, obviously, have a major impact on workers and other stakeholders alike.

In the UK, there is a well-established health and safety regulatory system. Companies and individuals can, therefore, face serious consequences when health and safety leadership falls short of what is required. Sanctions include fines, imprisonment and disqualification.

ACTIVITY

What do you think the reasons and business benefits are for effective health and safety leadership?

The following case studies from the HSE show what can happen with poor and good leadership.

LEADERSHIP CASE STUDIES

The HSE has highlighted a number of examples of weak health and safety leadership. In one such case, the HSE describes the fatal injury of a worker in a recycling firm employing approximately 30 people. The worker had been maintaining machinery that was not properly isolated and then started up unexpectedly, with fatal results.

Commenting on the case, HSE's investigating principal inspector said, "Evidence showed that the director chose not to follow the advice of his health and safety adviser and instead adopted a complacent attitude, allowing the standards in his business to fall."

As a result, the company director received a 12-month custodial sentence for manslaughter after an HSE and police investigation revealed there was no safe system of work for maintenance and that instruction, training and supervision were inadequate.[3]

Conversely, the HSE offers the example of British Sugar as a case study in the benefits to be gained by organisations through robust health and safety leadership.

The HSE says British Sugar had historically had an excellent safety record but in 2003 there were three fatalities at the company. Although health and safety had always been a business priority, the company recognised that a change in focus was needed. This included:

- the CEO assigning health and safety responsibilities to all directors;
- creating effective working partnerships with workers, trade unions and others;
- overseeing a behavioural change programme; and
- annual health and safety targets, and initiatives to meet these.

The results of the leadership-led changes included a two-thirds reduction in both lost times and minor injury frequency rates over a 10-year period, as well as much greater understanding by directors of health and safety risks.[4]

Behaviours/traits of a good health and safety leader

Taking the lead on health and safety initiatives

So what qualities should a good health and safety leader evidence? The behaviour of a health and safety leader is as or is more important than their attitude. A good health and safety leader will display a variety of behaviour that can positively influence the workforce. Very often they will not even be aware that they are doing this. Some of these types of behaviour include:

- encouraging communication (whether this be face-to-face or via other communication methods) with all workers regarding any health and safety anxieties the workers may have;

- making changes to improve working conditions (this is especially useful if the initial idea came from communications with the workforce; it shows that the leader has listened and, more importantly, acted to address the workers' anxieties);

- leading by example by showing the workforce that not only do they know the site health and safety rules but that they also model the correct health and safety behaviours;

- encouraging all levels of the workforce to understand and adhere to the site health and safety rules;

- being actively involved in health and safety committees and taking the lead on any health and safety campaigns/ initiatives that are being introduced;

- where unsafe working practices are taking place, advising the workers concerned about the possible consequences of their unsafe act and that working in such a way is unacceptable.

Developing an agreed health and safety vision for an organisation (health and safety leadership value 1)

> **ACTIVITY**
>
> - What would be appropriate for the health and safety vision of your own organisation?
>
> - Does the present version contain or take account of these factors?
>
> - List what you think the most important components might be.

You may have identified items such as a 'speak out' culture where everyone is encouraged to point out issues with health and safety wherever they encounter it. Or where all members of the workforce are inspired to take ownership of health and safety in the organisation. You may have identified communication as a vital component in the development of an agreed vision.

Needless to say, something as vital as an agreed health and safety vision or strategy will not be easy to implement. The effective leader will need to understand and balance points of view, overcome barriers and objections and listen carefully to what all stakeholders have to say, worker input is key.

A vision is about where you want to get to. Vision is not strategy. Vision is a 'where' and a 'what', while strategy is a 'how'. In developing your health and safety vison you may want to consider your organisation's values or stance on health and safety management eg, on corporate social responsibility. You may also discover that what you want your organisation's vision to be, is not what it currently is; as leaders, you are of course empowered to change this. For your vision to develop and grow, it will ideally build on what you are already successful at. Organisations can be very critical of themselves and sometimes forget to celebrate success. The term 'lessons learned' is not just about stopping things happening again, it is about making sure what is done well is repeated.

The most successful 'visions' tend to be simple, succinct and non-ambiguous. Workers and other stakeholders need to be able to easily understand and support the vision; this is difficult to do if it is overly complex or involved. An overly complex vison is an indication that it is trying to achieve too much and the quality and/or achievements will be diluted as energies and resources will be focused in different directions.

Although a vision should be looking to the future, it should also be time-bound so certain goals can be agreed and ultimately achieved. Each time a goal is achieved that success should be shared and celebrated with stakeholders, they are obviously key in turning the vision into reality.

Building and promoting a shared health and safety vision (health and safety leadership value 1)

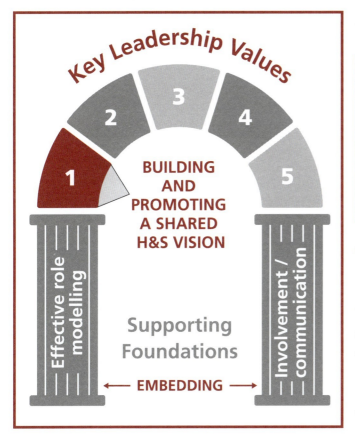

The key word here is 'shared'. It is vital that everyone feels part of the health and safety vision. It should not be something that people right across the organisation just comply with, it needs to be something to which they contribute. Their contribution must have equal value to all others.

For this to happen effectively it will require excellent communication, continuous consultation and discussion, reflection and feedback. Everyone should feel part of the process when establishing goals and objectives for their safety culture.

This should also clearly include shared responsibility; therefore, safety responsibilities need to be clearly defined. This needs to take place across each level of the organisation and should include the policies, goals and plans for the safety culture.

It is vital when building and promoting a shared vision that everyone involved is clear on what is happening, understands why and has the opportunity to comment or challenge when appropriate. It is also important that this health and safety vision is recognised as a long-term process; it should be something worth people buying into and not perceived as a 'quick fix' or box ticking exercise for compliance purposes. This will certainly be more credible if the leadership style adopted is responsive and considerate to all those involved.

> **ASSESSMENT ACTIVITY 1**
>
> - Please refer to the document Unit HSL1, guidance and information for candidates and internal assessors
>
> You should now complete task L1: Building and promoting a shared health and safety vision.

The characteristics that make a good health and safety leader

This could be a very long list and, unfortunately, can be somewhat discouraging for anyone aspiring to become an effective health and safety leader. You will also find many '10 Best Ways' '5 most effective…' '15 Top Tips…' all over the internet and of course many publications which will promise wonderful things.

For now, let us just say that we should regard many characteristics as learned skills and behaviours. It helps, however, to understand what leadership really means and we look at that in detail later on. However some of these characteristics include:

- relentlessly driving the health and safety message forward, not as an add-on but as a fundamental business imperative;
- being visible and proactive; and
- being able to articulate important messages across a wide variety of understanding and cultural mix.

1.2 The moral, legal and financial reasons for good health and safety leadership

Moral

The case for needing good health and safety leadership is often framed in terms of three basic reasons – moral, legal and financial.

RELIABILITY

INTEGRITY

HONESTY

CORE VALUES

SOCIAL RESPONSIBILITY

TRUST

COMMITMENT

TRANSPARENCY

CONNECTION

Societal expectations

There are many social issues that a good leader should be aware of that could affect their organisation.

Government initiatives and campaigns are aimed at the public to raise their understanding of health and safety issues. You may find that health and safety leaders are asked more questions as a result of such initiatives. Some examples of recent campaigns in the UK include the UK Health and Safety Executive's 'Helping Great Britain work well' strategy and campaigns such as the 'Go Home Healthy' campaign.

To try to prevent incidents from occurring in the first place, there is an expectation that health and safety leaders understand their organisation's risk profile. The HSE, in its guidance 'Managing for health and safety' (HSG65)[5] states that *"effective leaders and line managers know the risks their organisations face, rank them in order of importance and take action to control them. The range of risks goes beyond health and safety risks to include quality, environmental and asset damage, but issues in one area could impact in another"*. The risk profile should cover the:

- nature and level of the risks faced by the organisation;
- likelihood of adverse effects occurring and level of disruption;
- costs associated with each type of risk; and
- effectiveness of the controls in place to manage those risks.

Social media/the media in general, business globalisation and consumer choice all have a big part to play. Today the world is a much smaller place and most people tend to have a mobile communication device; stories are shared on social media, on the television, radio etc almost as soon as they break; this can sometimes be very damaging to an organisation's reputation. Consumers now have a much bigger say in the products that are on the market with many consumers now only buying brands that have been ethically produced or sourced.

As stated earlier, a good health and safety leader should be ensuring that sufficient control measures are in place to manage the organisation's health and safety risks. At the end of each working day, your workers (and their families) understandably expect to return home after being kept healthy and safe while at work.

Responsibility and accountability for health and safety

ISO 45001 is an agreed international standard for health and safety management systems. It represents an expectation of best practice. Clause 5.1 requires an organisation's leadership to take *"overall responsibility and accountability for the prevention of work-related injury and ill health as well as the provision of safe and healthy workplaces and activities"*. By taking responsibility for health and safety a good leader sends a clear message to the workforce that they care about the workers' health and safety. As this message flows through the organisation it can lead to positive changes, for example, by improving morale in the workforce which in turn could lead to an improved health and safety culture. Health and safety leaders should aim to make themselves as approachable and visible as possible within the organisation, for example, by conducting regular walkabouts.

Protection of workers from reprisals when reporting health and safety incidents and hazards

As stated earlier, the health and safety management system standard (ISO 45001) contains a clause relating to health and safety leadership. Part of this clause is to ensure the protection of workers when reporting health and safety incidents. As a leader you should be encouraging your workers to report all cases where they believe there is danger from an uncontrolled hazard, or if they have been involved in an incident (accident or near-miss). You should ensure that all managers, team leaders, supervisors etc understand your organisation's policy on reporting and that they should be encouraging workers under their control to report incidents. You can do this by, for example, ensuring that systems are in place for reporting (especially a near-miss reporting system), that the system is accessible by all workers, is easy and not time consuming to use and ensure that this message is cascaded down throughout the workforce. Feedback to the workforce on actions taken regarding reported incidents will go some way to proving to your workforce that you do want them to report and that no reprisals will be taken against them if they do report an incident.

Many countries also have legislation in place to protect their workers when reporting a health and safety incident or a hazard, eg, in the UK workers are protected under Regulation 44 of the Employment Rights Act 1996 ('protection from suffering detriment in employment') in relation to health and safety cases.

Legal

The role, function and limitations of legislation as a means of promoting health and safety performance

In simple terms, health and safety legislation is there to help to protect the health and safety of the workforce. It does this by imposing legal duties on employers and workers and a system of penalties (such as fines and imprisonment) for non-compliance. Although it should not be the only driver, the threat of these penalties can be a big motivator for better health and safety performance.

> **KEY TERMS**
>
> Legislation tends to be either:
>
> *goal setting* (sets objectives to be met, leaving the detail on exactly how to do this up to the employer); or
> *prescriptive* (tells organisations exactly what to do and when to do it).

Some of the limitations of using legislation to promote health and safety performance include:

- organisations ignoring best practice and only doing enough to meet the legal minimum requirements;

- health and safety can be seen by organisations as a regulatory and financial burden instead of a tool to help them protect their workforce;

- legislation (particularly prescriptive legislation) may not always keep pace with change and may not address current issues;

- the language used can sometimes be unclear and open to interpretation; and

- some organisations (especially those with inadequate health and safety assistance) may be unfamiliar with the law.

Element 1 The foundations of health and safety leadership

Content for UK students

As a leader there are specific pieces of legislation that can affect you and that you must be aware of. Ignorance is no defence when it comes to the law.

The Health and Safety at Work etc. Act 1974 (as amended)

The Act is goal setting. As a leader the main sections of the Act that you need to be aware of are Sections 2, 3, 36 and 37. The Act applies in England, Scotland and Wales; Northern Ireland is covered by the Health and Safety at Work (Northern Ireland) Order 1978. Where we refer to Section numbers, these refer to the Health and Safety at Work etc. Act 1974. The equivalent sections from the Northern Irish Order are as follows:

Health and Safety at Work etc. Act 1974	Health and Safety at Work (Northern Ireland) Order 1978
Section 2	Section 4
Section 3	Section 5
Section 36	Section 34
Section 37	Covered under Section 20(2) of the Interpretation Act (Northern Ireland) 1954. Section 34A of the 1978 Order amends the wording of Section 20(2) in relation to health and safety offences.

We will now look at the duties contained in each of these sections.

KEY TERMS

Reasonably practicable

Balancing the level of risk against the measures needed to control the real risk in terms of money, time or trouble. However, you do not need to take action if it would be grossly disproportionate to the level of risk.[6]

Section 2

The first part of this Section puts a duty on employers to protect the health, safety and welfare of all of their workers. The second part of this Section imposes specific duties and we will now look at each of these. Further information on what each of these duties requires can be found in the 'further information' box.

1. Provide and maintain safe equipment and systems of work as far as is reasonably practicable.

2. Storage, use, handling and transport of articles and substances: you must provide arrangements for ensuring, so far as is reasonably practicable, that safe working practices for these activities are in place.

3. The provision of information, instruction, training and supervision to ensure, so far as is reasonably practicable, the health and safety of all workers.

4. Any workplace that is under the employer's control must, as far as is reasonably practicable, be maintained in a safe condition so that it does not provide risk to the health and safety of all workers. The workplace must also have safe points of access and egress and these points must be maintained.

5. The provision and maintenance of a working environment that is, so far as is reasonably practicable, safe, without risks to health, and has adequate facilities and arrangements for the workers' welfare at work.

> **FURTHER INFORMATION**
>
> What do the duties under Section 2 of the Health and Safety at Work etc. Act 1974 mean?
>
> 1. Your will need to:
>
> - provide safe systems of work and procedures (written wherever possible) for the organisation's activities; and
>
> - make sure that not only is equipment bought that is manufactured to recognised standards/from a trusted source (look for the 'CE' mark or equivalent) but that it also undergoes regular maintenance and is withdrawn when it is deemed to be unsafe.

> 2. You should ensure that you have in place adequate control measures for storage, use, handling and transport of hazardous substances/articles. Such substances/articles can be identified from risk assessments and other sources of information such as Safety Data Sheets. As discussed in the previous paragraph, you should ensure that there are adequate written procedures for such activities. Issues associated with safe storage can include segregation of different types of hazardous substances, temperature requirements, loading/unloading procedures etc. When transporting hazardous substances, most countries have minimum requirements in the form of legislation for transportation equipment (containers and vehicles) and the use of competent workers in these operations.
>
> 3. To ensure the health and safety of all workers you must:
>
> - provide information and instruction to all workers regarding their work activities. This information can come from various sources such as risk assessments, machinery manuals, organisational policies, procedures, safe systems of work etc; and
>
> - ensure that your workforce receives adequate training and supervision in respect of the work activities that they carry out.
>
> 4. You must ensure that your workplace is maintained in a safe state, including safe entrance and exit points. This can be done by carrying out regular building maintenance activities and inspections to spot any potential risks before they escalate eg, do not wait for someone to trip over a loose carpet tile before getting it fixed or allow storage of equipment in front of fire exit doors which is only discovered during a fire drill.
>
> 5. You must provide and maintain welfare facilities such as toilets, washing facilities, clean drinking water, changing rooms (if applicable) etc. This applies to both fixed and temporary workplaces.

Organisations are also required to have a health and safety policy; if the organisation employs five or more workers this must be a written a policy that states how the organisation is going to manage health and safety. The policy must be brought to the attention of all workers. Further information on health and safety policy can be found on the HSE's website (http://www.hse.gov.uk/simple-health-safety/write.htm).

Section 2, also requires you to consult with workers on health and safety matters. The duty to consult is set out in legislation and further information can be found on the HSE's website (http://www.hse.gov.uk/workers/safetyrep.htm). Consultation will be discussed further later in this book.

The final part of the Section relates to forming a health and safety committee. It is good practice to set up a health and safety committee as this will involve the workforce in organisational health and safety matters. Further information on health and safety committees can be found on the HSE's website (http://www.hse.gov.uk/involvement/hscommittees.htm).

Section 3

Section 3 is very similar to Section 2 but it looks at the protection of 'others' who are not directly employed by the organisation but who could be affected by the organisation's work activities. For example, protection of temporary and contract workers, visitors to site and the general public.

The Act also imposes a duty on self-employed people to carry out their work so that other persons are not exposed to risks to their health or safety. However, self-employed people 'whose work activities pose no potential risk of harm to others' are now exempt from this Section of the Act.

The Act also requires employers, and qualifying self-employed people, to provide information to relevant parties on the way that they conduct the work activities that might affect the health and safety of others.

Section 36

This Section of the Act looks at offences committed by a 'person' (this could be an individual or an organisation) due to the act or default of some 'other person' (this could be a worker, manager, supervisor, contractor, consultant etc) then the 'other person' is guilty of the offence. In these cases the HSE could bring a prosecution against the 'person', the 'other person' or both. So, for example, if poor advice from a senior manager to a worker leads to a breach of duty, the senior manager could be prosecuted. The organisation may also be prosecuted but it would depend on the level of culpability. Prosecutions under Section 36 are not very common.

Section 37

This section will probably have the biggest impact on leaders; it means that senior directors/managers of an organisation can be individually liable for breaches of health and safety law and can be prosecuted as well as the organisation.

The wording from the Act states that it is for offences made by a 'body corporate' (an organisation). It must be proved that the offence was 'committed with the **consent or connivance** of, or have been attributable to any **neglect** on the part of any director, manager, secretary or other similar officers or a person who was purporting to act in any such capacity'. **Consent and connivance** is interpreted as having knowledge and making decisions based on that knowledge but turning a blind eye. In these circumstances **neglect** can include situations where a director ought to have been aware of the circumstances, in other words neglect does not require knowledge.

Recent years have seen a rise in Section 37 prosecutions and the sentences handed down. To illustrate this, a Section 37 case, which was prosecuted in November 2017, saw two company directors receiving prison sentences.

These sentences were given following a worker being killed when he was drawn into machinery at a recycling company. This was due to a fixed gate, which fenced off the area, being removed a number of weeks prior to the incident; this allowed workers free access to the area. The management of the company was aware that the gate was not in place.

- The Managing Director was sentenced to 20 weeks in prison (suspended for two years) and given a £50,000 fine.
- The former Operations Director of the company was sentenced to 20 weeks in prison (suspended for two years).

In addition to this the company was fined £880,000 plus costs of £100,000 for breaching Section 2 of the Health and Safety at Work Act. Further details about the case can be found here.[7]

Enforcement

Health and safety leaders do not want to be seeing the inside of a court room!

It is important for you to realise that the HSE can bring prosecutions against the organisation for breaches of Sections 2 and 3; these could result in substantial fines for the organisation (we will talk about this later when we discuss the application of the sentencing guidelines). Figures released by the HSE show in 2016/17 that fines from prosecutions where a conviction was achieved amounted to £69.9million. As well as prosecutions the cost of any civil claim brought against the organisation could also be substantial.

The Company Directors Disqualification Act 1986

If a director is found guilty of an offence (in this case Section 37 of the Health and Safety at Work Act etc. 1974), the court can make an order to disqualify the individual from 'the promotion, formation or management' of another organisation. The maximum period of disqualification is five years for a summary offence or 15 years for an indicatable offence.

KEY TERMS

England, Northern Ireland and Wales

A *'summary offence'* is a 'less serious' offence and is usually heard in Magistrates' Courts. The maximum sentence that a Magistrates' Court can hand down is an unlimited fine and/or up to six months' imprisonment.

An *'indictable offence'* is a more serious offence and is usually heard in the Crown Court. The maximum sentence that the Crown Court can hand down is an unlimited fine and/or up to two years' imprisonment.

Scotland

A *'summary offence'* is a 'less serious' offence and is usually heard in the Sherriff's Courts. The maximum sentence that can be handed down is a fine up to £10,000 and/or up to one year's imprisonment.

An *'solemn offence'* is a more serious offence and is usually heard in the Sherriff's Court. The maximum sentence that can be handed down is an unlimited fine and/or up to five years' imprisonment. If a sheriff decides that the maximum sentence at the sheriff court level isn't high enough, they can send the case to the High Court for sentencing. The maximum sentence that the High Court can hand down is an unlimited fine and up to life imprisonment.

Individual duties and possible enforcement actions for involuntary manslaughter/gross negligence

Involuntary manslaughter/gross negligence applies to an individual rather than the organisation. The offence is where someone is killed due to another person's extreme recklessness/carelessness. The maximum prison sentence for gross negligence manslaughter is life imprisonment.

There are four stages of 'legal test' that must be proved in order to bring a gross negligence manslaughter case:

- there must be a duty of care owed by the defendant to the deceased person;
- the defendant must have breached the duty of care;
- the breach must have caused or significantly contributed to the death of the deceased; and
- the breach must be characterised as gross negligence and, therefore, considered a crime.

A breach of duty of care happens when an individual, who owes the duty of care, does not act in the same way as a reasonable person would do in the same position. Therefore, if the individual was acting within the range of what was generally accepted as standard behaviour/practice, it will be difficult to prove that they have breached the duty of care.

When looking at work-related deaths, very often proceedings are also taken against the individual under Sections 7 (which is not part of this course), 36 or 37 of the Health and Safety at Work Act.

EXAMPLE

Gross negligence manslaughter case

In May 2017 a company director was sentenced to 32 months' imprisonment when he admitted causing the death of a golf club worker. The worker was 29 years old and had ADHD and learning difficulties. He died while collecting golf balls from an eight-foot deep lake with a weighted belt and breathing equipment; the breathing equipment was lost during the dive. The golf worker was paid £20 to £40 per day instead of the defendant employing a trained diver that would have cost approximately £1000 day. The director had stood and watched the incident happen and only raised the alarm when he saw a constant stream of bubbles rising to the lake's surface and saw that the floatation device carrying the air supply floated to the side of the lake. The director admitted to manslaughter by gross negligence.[8]

Sentencing for gross negligence manslaughter cases

These guidelines were published in 2018 and apply to all cases sentenced on or after 1 November 2018 no matter when the offence occurred. These guidelines apply to England and Wales only. The maximum sentence for gross negligence manslaughter cases is life imprisonment.

If the accused is found guilty, the judge will need to pass sentence. When sentencing, the judge considers:

- the offence category (defendant's culpability); and
- the sentence starting point and category range.

The offence category range is 1– 18 years in prison, with the starting points ranging from 2 to 12 years:

	Culpability			
	A	B	C	D
Starting point	12 years	8 years	4 years	2 years
Category range	10–18 years	6–12 years	3–7 years	1–4 years

Where it is not clear which offence category a case falls into, the judge can adjust the starting point. These adjustments are applied before any other adjustments for aggravating or mitigating features of the case.

Culpability ranges:

A	B	C	D
Very high	High	Medium	Lower

Once the starting point has been set, the judge will then go on to consider other issues that could either increase or decrease the sentence. These issues include:

- statutory or other aggravating factors, eg time elapsed since previous conviction(s) (statutory factor) or offender ignored previous warnings (other factors);
- mitigating factors, eg attempts to assist the victim;
- assistance given to the prosecution;
- guilty plea(s);
- dangerousness (when considering a life or extended sentence); and
- the totality principle (is the total sentence (if more than one offence) proportionate to the overall offending behaviour?).

The judge should also:

- decide whether to consider making a compensation/ ancillary orders;
- give reasons for and explain the effect of the sentence; and
- take account of any time spent on bail or as tagged curfew.

Further information on the guidelines can be found here: https://www.sentencingcouncil.org.uk/wp-content/uploads/Manslaughter-definitive-guideline-Web.pdf

The Corporate Manslaughter and Corporate Homicide Act 2007

The legislation is about holding the organisation accountable rather than individual directors. As we have already discussed, individuals can be prosecuted under gross negligence manslaughter charges or under various sections of the Health and Safety at Work Act.

The offence of corporate manslaughter/homicide can be brought:

- when the way in which an organisation's activities are managed or organised cause a person's death and amount to a gross breach of a relevant duty of care owed by the organisation to the deceased; and
- if the way in which its activities are managed or organised by its senior management is a substantial element of the death.

The offence is, therefore, aimed at the strategic/top level management of an organisation rather than activities conducted by junior level workers (in other words the organisation's leaders).

The offence of corporate manslaughter/homicide is an indictable offence which can only be heard in the High Court.

The penalties available to the Court when an organisation is found guilty are:

- a fine (which we will discuss next in the sentencing guidelines section); and/or
- a remedial order; and/or
- a publicity order.

A remedial order can be handed down on a guilty conviction which will require the organisation to remedy:

- the breach of the duty of care;
- anything that looks like it may have caused the death; and
- any deficiencies in the organisation's health and safety systems that the offence highlights.

The Court can also hand down a publicity order. This will require the organisation to publicise:

- that it has been convicted of the offence;
- the details of the offence;
- the amount of any fine; and
- the terms of the remedial order (if applicable).

The organisation can be ordered to publicise details of the offence on their website or by taking out an advertisement in the local press or in trade publications/websites. If the organisation does not comply with the publicity order this is also an indictable offence and could result in an unlimited fine should the organisation be found guilty.

EXAMPLE

Corporate Manslaughter convictions

The first Corporate Manslaughter case was sentenced in 2011 following an incident in September 2008. A geologist employed by an organisation was investigating soil conditions in a trench; the trench collapsed and killed the worker. The organisation was successfully prosecuted and received a fine of £385,000 payable over 10 years.[9]

One of the biggest fines to date was given after a guilty verdict for Corporate Manslaughter was handed down to a plant hire company. One of their workers was driving a heavy crane which experienced a malfunction with its brakes causing it to crash into an earth bank and fall from the road. The company was found guilty of Corporate Manslaughter and also two offences under the Health and Safety at Work etc Act 1974 (breaches of Sections 2 and 3). In December 2015 the company was fined £700,000 and ordered to pay costs of £200,000.[10]

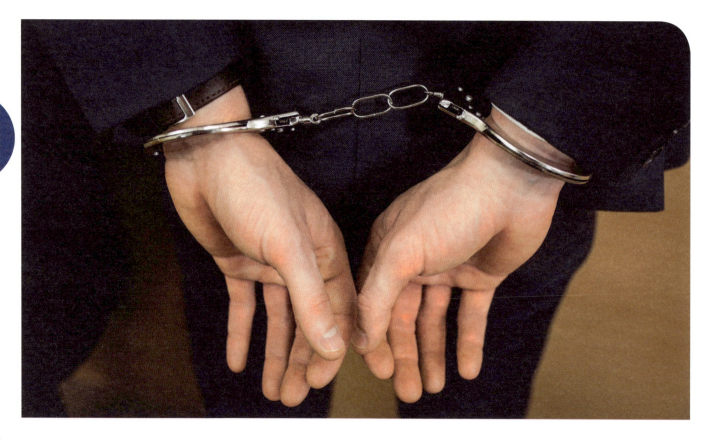

The Health and Safety Offences and Corporate Manslaughter sentencing guidelines

Sentencing in England, Wales and Northern Ireland

The Guidelines were published by the Sentencing Council in February 2016 and became applicable for all offences sentenced after 1 February 2016, no matter when the offence was committed. The Guidelines are applicable to England and Wales only. However, courts in Northern Ireland can refer to the Guidelines as a starting point when sentencing.

> **KEY TERMS**
>
> **Culpability**[11] how much the defendant is at fault for the offence. This ranges from very high to low. High is where there was a deliberate breach or a flagrant disregard for the law. Low is where it is found that failings were minor and occurred as an isolated incident.
>
> **Harm category**[12] Levels 1 to 4, with 1 being the most severe. The harm level is based on two factors, the harm that occurred (levels A to C) and the likelihood (high, medium or low) of the harm occurring.
>
> Level A: death or an injury which will result in life long care being needed.
> Level B: includes physical or mental impairment, not requiring lifelong care, but which has a substantial and long-term effect on the sufferer's ability to carry out normal day-to-day activities or on their ability to return to work; or a progressive, permanent or irreversible condition.
> Level C: includes all other cases not falling within Level A or Level B.

The guidelines give a range of sentences that are appropriate for each type of offence (offence ranges). For each offence there are a number of categories that reflect varying degrees of seriousness. For each category there is a starting point for sentencing.

When deciding on the level of fine the judge must consider the following:

- the level of culpability of the defendant;
- the level of harm created by the offence;
- the number of workers or members of the public exposed to the risk AND whether the breach was a significant cause of actual harm.

The level of fine is based on the organisation's **turnover**, not profit. There are five categories of organisation:

- micro (turnover of not more than £2million) organisations;
- small (turnover between £2million and £10million);
- medium (turnover between £10million and £50million);
- large (turnover of £50million or more); or
- 'very large organisations' that have a turnover which greatly exceeds £50million can be fined outside of the normal ranges should the offence warrant this.

When sentencing, the judge will look at the starting point for the fine but will also take into account if there are any factors where an increase or reduction in the fine can be made. The table below gives a few examples of the level of fine that **organisations** can expect to see based on the above factors.

Level of culpability	Harm category	Size of organisation	Fine starting point	Maximum fine	Minimum fine
Very high	1	Large	£4million	£10million	£2.6million
High	4	Large	£240,000	£700,000	£120,000
Very high	1	Medium	£1.6million	£4million	£1million
Low	2	Medium	£40,000	£100,000	£14,000
High	3	Small	£54,000	£210,000	£25,000
Medium	2	Small	£54,000	£230,000	£25,000
Very high	1	Micro	£250,000	£450,000	£150,000
Medium	2	Micro	£30,000	£70,000	£14,000

For Corporate Manslaughter offences there is an unlimited maximum fine but the offence range is from £180,000 to £20million. As with fines for health and safety offences, the fine is payable by the organisation. An offence that is considered to be level 'A' (where the organisation is deemed to have a high level of culpability) for a 'large organisation' would have a starting point of £7.5million with the category range between £4.8million and £20million.

As we mentioned earlier, in the book, individuals can be prosecuted as well as organisations. As with organisations, fines are based on the culpability of the individual. However, it is also important to note that individuals could also receive a jail term for the most serious offences. Summary offences can attract an unlimited fine and/or up to six months' custodial sentence. An indicatable offence will also attract an unlimited fine but the jail term for these offences could be up to two years.

For example, where an individual is found guilty and was found to be very highly culpable, the following sentences (depending on the harm category) could apply:

Harm category	Sentence starting point	Category range
1	18 months' custody	1 - 2 years' custody
2	1 year's custody	26 weeks - 18 months' custody
3	26 weeks' custody	Band F fine* or high level community order - 1 year's custody
4	Band F fine	Band E fine - 26 weeks' custody

* Fines are split into six bands; the starting point for each band is as follows:

Band A – 50% of relevant weekly income
Band B – 100% of relevant weekly income
Band C – 150% of relevant weekly income
Band D – 250% of relevant weekly income
Band E – 400% of relevant weekly income
Band F – 600% of relevant weekly income

Therefore, a director earning £98,000 per annum (£1885 per week) could find themselves with a personal fine starting at around £11,500 when the harm category is 4.

Sentencing in Scotland

Scotland does not currently have any official guidelines but there are 'sentencing factors' which the judge can consider.

The Scottish Sentencing Council have drawn up a wide range of factors which judges should generally consider when deciding on a sentence. The judge will decide:

- which factors presented to the court are relevant and should be taken into account; and
- what weight to give to each factor; these can be aggravating factors (which will make the sentence more severe) and mitigating factors (which will make the sentence less severe).

Some of the general factors which can be consider are:

- the type and seriousness of the crime;
- the culpability of those involved;
- protection of public and deterrence; and
- personal circumstances of the offender.

Some of the aggravating factors which the judge will take account of include:

- the effects of the crime on the victim(s); and
- past convictions.

Some of the mitigating factors which the judge will take account of include:

- whether the offender pleaded guilty;
- first offence (if no crime has previously been committed the sentence will usually be less server); and
- whether the offender assisted the prosecutor after entering a guilty plea.

The following table gives an overview of the sentences available in the various levels of Scottish Court (the Procurator Fiscal will decide which court the case will be heard in):

	Justice of the Peace Court	Sheriff Court (summary)	Sheriff Court (solemn)	High Court
Who decides the verdict?	Justice of the Peace	Sheriff	Jury	Jury
Who sets the sentence?	Justice of the Peace	Sheriff	Sheriff	Judge
Maximum fine available	Up to £2,500	Up to £10,000	Unlimited	Unlimited
Maximum length of imprisonment	Up to 60 days	Up to 1 year	Up to 5 years	Up to life

Sheriffs/judges are able to impose a fine and/or imprisonment depending on the offence. The courts can also hand down community based sentences.

For more information on the sentencing factors please refer to guidance from the Scottish Sentencing Council[13].

EXAMPLE

Recent fines for health and safety offences

In January 2017 a retail company was fined £2.2million and ordered to pay costs of £71,000. The fine was due to a worker being injured by a cage falling over which left the worker paralysed below the hip with only a 1% chance of ever walking again. The level of culpability in the case was set at high with a harm category of 2. The organisation's turnover was way in excess of that for large companies so the judge treated this case as a 'very large organisation'. When sentencing the judge took into account the guilty plea and other mitigating circumstances.

Also in January 2017 a food manufacturer was fined £2million and ordered to pay costs of £20,000. The offence was that a worker sustained a spinal fracture after falling nearly 2 metres from the top of a mixing machine while attempting to clean it. The company's turnover put them in the 'very large organisation' category but the judge decided to treat the organisation as 'large'. The culpability level was high and the harm category was 1. The starting point for the fine would, therefore, have been £2.4million with a category range of between £1.5million and £6million.

Content for international students

Different levels of standards and enforcement in different jurisdictions

There are different standards of health and safety around the world; some countries have mature, well-embedded systems while other countries have very rudimentary systems or no system at all. Organisations that operate globally can find this frustrating; what meets the standard in some countries will not in others. Some larger organisations will, therefore, use standards from countries with a robust system to manage their risks wherever they are operating in the world. When tendering for large projects, their systems of work, policies, procedures etc will reference these higher standards. These organisations are sometimes seen as leaders within the country of operation; once the local workforce sees that better standards are available they are more likely to start demanding this from other organisations.

Having a robust regulatory system in place (including an enforcement regime), for the majority of organisations, is a big incentive to provide better health and safety standards for their workforce.

Element 1 **The foundations of health and safety leadership**

The International Organization for Standardization (ISO) has recently published an occupational health and safety management systems standard (ISO 45001:2018); ISO 45001 is the successor to OHSAS 18001. The standard is recognised globally and provides a framework for organisations to use to manage their health and safety risks. As all organisations will have to evidence how they meet each of the clauses within the standard, this can also be seen as a driver to improve health and safety standards globally.

The International Labour Organisation (ILO) http://www.ilo.org/global/lang--en/index.htm has drawn up over 40 conventions and recommendations and produced over 40 codes of practice relating to occupational health and safety. These conventions/codes of practice give the minimum standard that countries and organisations should be looking to implement. However, the issue here is that there is no policing of standards within the countries who have ratified the convention. No policing usually means no enforcement actions are taken, which in turn disincentives countries/organisations from improving health and safety standards. As we discussed earlier, there may be different standards of health and safety around the globe due to countries interpreting the language of the convention in different ways.

Responsibilities of leaders under Article 20 of the C155 Occupational Health and Safety Convention 1981

As discussed earlier, the ILO established the above convention in 1981. The convention requires each member state to have a *"coherent national policy on occupational safety, occupational health and working environment"*. Article 20 of the convention requires *"Co-operation between management and workers and/or their representatives within the undertaking ..."*. Health and safety leaders should, therefore, be proactive and be seen to be engaging with the workforce whenever possible (we will discuss methods of engagement later in this book). Workers are more likely to co-operate with the employer when leadership is visible and is interested in the workforce.

Financial

The level of fines/penalties/compensation

As we discussed in Section 2 the level of fines in the UK following the introduction of the 'sentencing guidelines' have risen dramatically over the last few years. However, organisations should be aware that not only are there fines to consider but there could also be costs associated with:

- fees charged by regulators;
- putting right anything identified in enforcement notices;
- the cost of non-production should a prohibition notice be served by a regulator;
- loss of business and reputation should any enforcement action be publicised;
- level of compensation/damages due to injured parties.

The real cost of accidents/incidents

Each year millions of days are lost due to workplace accidents and ill-health. Each year, the UK Health and Safety Executive publishes health and safety statistics. The following statistics will give you an idea of the size of the health and safety issue in the UK (the statistics have been averaged out over a five-year period):

Work-related illness	1.2million
Mesothelioma deaths	2,484
Fatalities	141
Non-fatal injuries to workers	612,250
RIDDOR injuries	74,927
Musculoskeletal disorders	503,000
Work-related stress, depression or anxiety	470,800
Lost working days due to work-related illness and injury	28.82million

The cost to the UK of these injuries and ill-health is, on average, £14.26billion per annum.

These figures are also reflected globally. The International Labour Organisation (ILO) has produced the following statistics. However, it should be noted that not all nations affiliated with the ILO report health and safety figures.

Annual deaths due to work-related accidents or diseases	>2.78million
Non-fatal work-related injuries and illness	374million

The following statistics have been averaged over a five year period:

Average fatalities from occupational injury per year	17,500
Non-fatal occupational injuries	9.7million
Days lost due to occupational injury	66.5million

The annual cost to the global economy is estimated to be 3.94% of global Gross Domestic Product.

Taking this down a level to that of the organisation we have already discussed the level of fines likely to be seen within the UK. However, there are many other costs that also need to be considered. Some costs can be insured against but the majority of costs incurred are not covered by insurance and must be absorbed by the organisation.

It is estimated that the ratio of insured v uninsured costs is roughly 1:8 (so for every £1 of insurance payment the organisation receives they will pay out a minimum of £8 but could be as much as £36). The analogy that is very often drawn is comparing costs to an iceberg. The tip of the iceberg, visible above water, represents insured costs but the majority of the iceberg, which is hidden under the water, represents the uninsured costs.

The hidden costs of accidents

Examples of costs that you can insure against are:

- medical costs relating to injury and/or ill-health; and
- damages to the injured party or to the family of a deceased worker.

In the UK the insurable costs are covered through compulsory employers' liability insurance.

Some examples of costs which are uninsurable are:

- delays in production;
- additional wage bills for overtime payments/temporary workers to cover the injured person's job;
- sick pay for the injured person;
- loss of contracts resulting from either loss of reputation and/or being unable to meet orders due to production down-time;
- damage to equipment, plant, products or premises;
- fines;
- legal expenses (own or the prosecution's);
- investigation time and site clear up costs; and
- excess of any insurance claim.

How leaders can gain assurance that health and safety is being managed effectively

The Health and Safety Executive, in association with the Institute of Directors, produced a set of guidelines for organisations to assist in giving assurance to leadership teams that the organisation's health and safety practices are being managed effectively. These guidelines[14], which you are encouraged to read, provide more detail on this vital component of health and safety culture.

Context of the organisation

Boardroom decisions must be made in the context of the organisation's health and safety policy; it is important to 'design-in' health and safety when implementing decisions. Identifying who is a stakeholder with regards to an organisation is also key; as we know, stakeholders extend further than internal workers. For example, suppliers, local communities, customers etc can all be consulted with (when identified that it would be appropriate to do so), and they can provide some valuable insight.

Suppliers and contractors also have specialist knowledge that can be vital when introducing change. It is important to remember that often, it is also these people who are the last to know when work-based changes have been introduced, and any changes undertaken can directly affect their activities on a work site.

The context of the organisation is also a clause from ISO 45001:2018 (Health and safety management system).

Risk profiling

The risk profile of an organisation should inform all aspects of the approach to leading and managing health and safety risks.

Every organisation will have its own risk profile and effective leaders must know the risks their organisations face, rank them in order of importance and take action to control them. This is the starting point for determining the greatest health and safety issues for an organisation. In some businesses the risks will be tangible and with immediate obvious safety hazards. In other organisations the risks may be health-related and it may be a long time before any illness becomes apparent.

In essence, a risk profile examines the nature and levels of threats faced by an organisation. It examines the likelihood of adverse effects occurring, the level of disruption and costs associated with each type of risk and the effectiveness of the control measures in place.

Health and safety leaders need to ensure that their respective organisations have built a risk profile that covers:

- the nature and level of the threats faced by an organisation;
- the likelihood of adverse effects occurring;
- the level of disruption and costs associated with each type of risk; and
- the effectiveness of controls in place to manage those risks.

The outcome of risk profiling will be that the right risks have been identified and prioritised for action, controls communicated, with minor risks not given too much priority. It also informs decisions about what risk control measures are needed and where resources should be made available and allocated.

Further information on risk profiling can be found in the HSE's publication 'Managing for health and safety' (HSG65)[5].

Management system thinking

Good health and safety management does not happen by accident. Management of health and safety in any type of organisation requires clearly defined processes. An effective health and safety management system will help an organisation meet legal obligations, as it will assist compliance with legislation and any internal corporate standards eg, the health and safety management system ISO 45001.

An effective HSMS is the product of a structured and focused effort that places health and safety at the centre of business decisions and not as an after-thought. There are many different models of HSMS, but all follow the same plan-do-check-act cycle (known as 'PDCA') as part of a continual improvement process. In the PDCA cycle, the following broad steps are taken:

- **plan** - establish a clear set of goals and targets that will move the organisation forward in terms of health and safety management;

- **do** - carry out actions to improve health and safety;
- **check** - monitor and determine whether the steps you have taken are moving you closer to your goals; and
- **act** - take action as a result of the monitoring findings in order to continually improve.

In terms of an HSMS (for example, ISO45001:2018), these steps are broken down under:

- context of the organisation (discussed earlier in this section);
- leadership and worker participation (HSMS framework);
- planning (plan);
- support (do);
- operation (do);
- performance evaluation (check); and
- improvement (act).

Health and safety management systems sections

Leadership (underpinning all clauses of the HSMS)

This is a new clause within ISO45001 and it requires that organisations evidence how their leadership commit to the HSMS. There are many points that an organisation must consider that range from taking overall responsibility for health and safety, promoting continual improvement etc. If your organisation has a formalised HSMS, you find that, as a health and safety leader, you will be invited to take part in both internal and external audits to evidence how you meet this clause.

It is also important that you should be involved in the implementation of the health and safety policy. The policy should be a clear demonstration of the aims of the organisation towards health and safety, together with the vision and commitment to achieve these goals. It should also commit to complying with legislation and to continually improve processes. It should come from board level. As part of the policy you will also be expected to assign roles and responsibilities for health and safety throughout the organisation.

Another important part of the leadership clause is consultation with the workforce and gaining worker participation. It is really important that your workers are consulted on anything that could affect their health and safety eg, implementation of new work equipment. You should also engage your workforce and encourage them to take part in health and safety-related activities. For example, get them involved in the risk assessment process; the workers are carrying out their work activities and are, therefore, best placed to help you understand the hazards and risks associated with their work.

Planning (plan)

This should include the processes for the identification of hazards and the reduction of risks. The plan should then seek to deliver a reduction in risk while prioritising the biggest issues. At the same time, the plan should also identify potential breaches of, or changes in, legislation/compliance obligations, and address these too. You should also ensure that you consider all risks and opportunities associated with the HSMS eg, a risk to the HSMS could be an ineffective audit programme; an opportunity could be bringing in technology to improve health and safety performance by using technology to automate higher risk activities.

Support (do)

This section of the HSMS looks at resources, competence, awareness, communication and document control. It is the health and safety leader's responsibility to ensure that there are adequate resources provided to implement or maintain the HSMS. You should also ensure that the workforce is aware of relevant information relating to the HSMS, eg, that they know what is contained in your organisation's health and safety policy, the implications of not conforming to the HSMS etc. It is also really important that competence levels of all workers throughout the organisation are determined; if any gaps in knowledge or skills is identified you should ensure that the workers receive appropriate training. Any documents relating to the HSMS should be adequately controlled. If your organisation has a formal quality management system (QMS) you can integrate this requirement with the QMS.

Operation (do)

You will need to ensure that processes (written or physical) or put into place to eliminate hazards with reference to the hierarchy of control (eliminate, substitute, engineering controls, administrative controls, issue of personal protective equipment as a last resort).

The clause also looks at the management of change, whether the change is temporary or permanent. As a leader you should ensure that processes are in place and that any possible consequences of the change have been taken into account.

Organisations are also required to control their contractors from the tendering stage right through to the end of the work. Leaders should ensure that contactors are provided with all relevant information regarding the identified hazards on site. This also refers to outsourced activities.

The final requirement of this clause is emergency preparedness; again, you should be ensuring that your organisation has in place plans to deal with any potential emergencies and that these plans are tested on a regular basis, and updated as and when required.

Performance evaluation (check)

In order to determine if progress is being made towards the goals, there should be monitoring and measurement activities carried out. These will include active and reactive measures (also known as 'leading' and 'lagging' indicators), the most widely used are accident data (lagging) and statistical trends. Leading indicators (eg planned maintenance) are important as they can identify potential problems before an incident occurs. As well as monitoring against the targets, there should also be assessments to determine whether compliance obligations are being complied with.

The organisation should also have in place a robust internal audit programme that should establish the scope and frequency of the audit.

We have already talked about compliance with legislation and standards. This part of the clause is to ensure that regular compliance evaluations are carried out. So you will need to ensure that you have you identified all relevant compliance obligations AND can evidence how you meet each obligation.

The final part of this clause is for management to carry out regular reviews of the management system to review the data and ensure that the plan remains relevant to feed the continual improvement process. This should lead to action, as necessary, to correct any identified issues.

Improvement (act)

The organisation should be looking to (continually) improve the performance of the HSMS. To do this you will need to be looking at any non-conformances that may be identified via audit or some other method such as complaints from workers. You should also ensure that any accidents and (very importantly) near misses are thoroughly investigated. This should help to stop the incident from occurring again in the future. Any additional controls implemented should be reviewed to ensure their continuing suitability.

The organisation should also consider any other improvements that could be made. Suggestions that come from the workforce are usually invaluable; the health and safety leader should not discount these and only expect solutions to come from the top.

Leadership team involved, informed and visible

Today's workplaces are increasingly complex and the demands on all levels of management, especially senior leaders, grows ever more acute. As a result, leaders need to rely more than ever on the intelligence, resourcefulness and competence of their teams and workers. Collaboration is an essential ingredient within a strong health and safety culture. Collaboration leads to gains in morale, realises creativity, changes attitudes and behaviours and gets 'buy in' to new initiatives and targets. Collaboration also helps to keep leaders informed as to current challenges with regards to health and safety management. More importantly, leaders remain visibly engaged with health and safety initiatives and demonstrate how important they are to organisational objectives.

Being visible and taking the time to be seen, is not about checking on workers; effective leaders schedule time to engage with workers, in order to determine that they are receiving the care and attention that they deserve. Witnessing work in action also helps a leader to determine if workers are properly trained. Working side-by-side with workers also gives a leader an opportunity, to explore concerns and communicate a health and safety vision in an informal way.

Leadership visibility and involvement can also be demonstrated by:

- health and safety appearing regularly on the agenda for board meetings;
- a chief executive giving the clearest visibility of leadership, but some organisations find it useful to name one of their senior leaders as the health and safety 'champion';
- the presence on the board of a health and safety director can be a strong signal that health and safety is taken seriously and that its strategic importance is understood; and
- senior leaders setting health and safety targets helps define what an organisation is seeking to achieve.

Governance, competency and resource

For many organisations, health and safety is a corporate governance issue. The leaders should integrate health and safety into the main governance structures, including board sub-committees, such as risk, remuneration and audit. Organisations should have robust systems of internal control, covering not just financial risks but also risks relating to the environment, business reputation and health and safety. Health and safety management must of course be adequately resourced. A famous quote from Trevor Kletz, one of the pioneers of process safety management, is:

> "…if you think safety is expensive, try an accident."

This is very true, but more importantly, people also get hurt, and sadly sometimes killed. Damage to workers' health can be catastrophic too, with lives cut short or debilitated due to workplace exposures.

Resource spent on ensuring competency within the workplace is rarely wasted. A competent person is someone who has sufficient high quality training and experience or knowledge and other qualities that allow them to assist an organisation to achieve its aims. The level of competence required will depend on the complexity of the situation and the particular skill set needed. Certainly, with regards to health and safety management, it is essential competent advice is available, be that internal to an organisation, or bought in.

Approval and monitoring of performance indices

As explored above, in order to determine how well an organisation is performing with regards to health and safety management, leading and lagging indicators must be measured.

Leaders can use leading and lagging indicators to ensure that:

- appropriate weight is given to reporting both preventive information (such as progress of training and maintenance programmes) and incident data (such as accident and sickness absence rates);
- periodic audits of the effectiveness of management structures and risk controls for health and safety are carried out;

- the impact of changes such as the introduction of new procedures, work processes or products, or any major health and safety failure, is reported as soon as possible to the board; and

- there are procedures to implement new and changed legal requirements and to consider other external developments and events.

Continuous improvement

All good organisations strive to improve performance, an advantage to managing health and safety is that there is also strong evidential links to improved quality as a result of a strong health and safety culture. As described above, following a management review, the last step of any PDCA cycle is continual improvement as we look to implement any identified improvements.

As we know, continuous improvement is something that is essential within any organisation intending long-term success. What is essential with regards to health and safety management is how an identified improvement is implemented. By being very clear as to why the change is being introduced, it will be more readily accepted and adopted by workers. Additionally, organisations should have robust procedures in place for any change management process; these should consider the implication of any 'change' prior to it being put into practice.

Horizon scanning

With regards to health and safety management, horizon scanning can be used to detect early signs of potentially important developments and opportunities, with emphasis on new technology and its effects on the workplace. For example, is new equipment being developed that could be introduced to the workplace in order to reduce risk? Organisations also need to be aware of any upcoming changes in law or other compliance obligations, so they can anticipate changes and consider their response.

Benchmarking of organisational health and safety performance

Health and safety benchmarking is used to assess health and safety performance of an organisation by comparing it with that of other high performing companies within their industry. Benchmarking allows organisations, with common interests with regards to health and safety, to identify and implement possible improvements. Organisations that undertake benchmarking achieve the following benefits:

- each organisation learns from the other ways in which it could improve the delivery of health and safety and plan ways to implement those improvements;

- each organisation would gain a better understanding of its own (and other) processes for dealing with health and safety that could be built on subsequently to develop suitable performance measures and targets; and

- successful benchmarking partnerships can aid future health and safety improvements.

Notes

1.4 How good leadership can positively influence health and safety culture

Good leadership and effective leadership techniques should have a positive impact on the culture of any organisation. This of course should include the health and safety culture of an organisation. Elsewhere in this book you will discover how effective leadership and the use of appropriate tools and techniques will provide opportunities to influence behaviour, set examples and ensure that everyone's voice is heard regarding health and safety matters. Without positive influential leadership it will prove difficult, or indeed, impossible to ensure the right culture is systematically maintained.

The meaning of safety culture

> **KEY TERMS**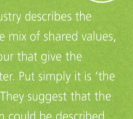
>
> *Safety culture*
>
> The Confederation of British Industry describes the culture of an organisation as "the mix of shared values, attitudes and patterns of behaviour that give the organisation its particular character. Put simply it is 'the way we do things round here'". They suggest that the 'safety culture' of an organisation could be described as the ideas and beliefs that all members of the organisation share about risk, accidents and ill health".[15]

But what is a 'safety culture' and how do we know if we have one?

Safety culture must ultimately be part of a larger organisational culture, but what is that? It has been said that organisational culture is easier to 'feel' or experience than to describe. Unlike organisational structure it does not have a formal recognisable shape, tall or flat for example. It has sometimes been described as 'the way we do things around here'. Charles Handy has written many books on the subject of culture. His volume 'Understanding Organisations' is still used extensively to help try and make sense of how organisational culture works within a structure to influence the way an organisation, as well as all those within it, work together. This is quite complex material, but extremely useful for any effective leader to understand. Clearly the organisational culture will have significant influence over the 'safety culture'.

We will look in detail at human failure (errors and violations) later in this book, as it is important for health and safety leaders to understand human failure and the differences between errors and violations. Human failure is not random, there are distinct patterns and types of human failure with different causes and therefore different ways of addressing them eg, forgetting an essential step in a task due to fatigue vs an operator cutting a corner in a procedure due to productivity requirements. As a leader the important thing is to fully understand the root cause of the failure and understand the local context of the individual at the sharp end of the failure.

You must also bear in mind that errors will happen, after all we are only human! How you deal with these as a leader could directly influence the safety culture within the organisation. Again, this comes back to a 'just culture' and ensuring that these situations are handled consistently through all levels of the organisation.

The problem with culture, in this case safety culture, is that it is hard to measure, and therefore to understand what needs to be changed and how to go about making the changes so that everyone involved will benefit.

The table on the next page provides a checklist of positive actions that underpin a positive safety culture. Broadly speaking this would indicate that an organisation had a 'good' safety culture.

A healthy safety culture is one where there is…	this is shown when management…	… and is helped when management…
Visible Commitment to Safety by Management	➢ Make regular *useful* visits to site ➢ Discuss safety matters with frontline personnel ➢ Will stop production for safety reasons regardless of cost ➢ Spend time and money on safety e.g. to provide protective equipment, safety training, and conduct safety culture workshops or audits ➢ Will not tolerate violations of procedures and actively try to improve systems so as to discourage violations e.g. plan work so that short cuts aren't necessary to do the work in time.	➢ Makes time to visit site (not just following an accident or incident) ➢ All show commitment ➢ Has good non-technical skills (e.g. communication skills;) ➢ Are also interested in workforce safety when they are not at work, e.g. provide information on domestic safety ➢ Shows concern for wider issues e.g. workforce stress and general health ➢ Actively sets an example (e.g. always conform to all safety procedures)
Workforce Participation and Ownership of Safety Problems and Solutions	➢ Consults widely about health and safety matters ➢ Does more than the minimum to comply with the law on consultation ➢ Seeks workforce participation in: • setting policies and objectives • accident/near miss investigations	➢ Supports an active safety committee ➢ Have a positive attitude to safety representatives ➢ Provides tools or methods that encourage participation e.g. behavioural observation programmes & incentive schemes that promote safety
Trust Between Shop floor and Management	➢ Encourages all employees and contractors to challenge anyone working on site about safety without fear of reprisals ➢ Keeps their promises ➢ Treats the workforce with respect	➢ Promotes job satisfaction/good industrial relations and high morale ➢ Promotes a 'just' culture (assigning blame only where someone was clearly reckless or took a significant risk) ➢ Encourages trust between all employees
Good Communications	➢ Provides good (clear, concise, relevant) written materials (safety bulletins, posters, guidance) ➢ Provides good briefings on current issues day to day and in formal safety meetings; listening and feedback	➢ Encourages employee participation in suggesting safety topics to be communicated ➢ Provides specific training in communication skills ➢ Has more than one means of communicating
A Competent Workforce	➢ Ensures that everyone working on their sites is competent in their job and in safety matters	Is supportive Has a good competence assurance system

Source: HSE Human Factors Briefing Note No. 7, safety culture [16]

Promoting fairness and trust in relationships with others (health and safety leadership value 4)

Promoting fairness and trust at 'grass roots' level

> **ASSESSMENT ACTIVITY 2**
>
> Please refer to the document Unit HSL1, guidance and information for candidates and internal assessors.
>
> You should now complete task **L4: Promoting fairness and trust in relationships with others.**

Trust is something that is generally earned. Building a relationship based on trust and fairness obviously requires that a leader must not only possess those qualities but also visibly demonstrate them. There is no point in talking up openness, honesty and integrity unless you are prepared to lead using these qualities. Failure to do so opens the way for accusations of hypocrisy and, as can be evidenced by the many occasions where hypocrisy can be witnessed in many areas of public life, it is difficult to recover from and impossible to build trust once insincerity has been identified. The effective leader in health and safety must lead from the front and lead by 'doing' not just by saying. Sharing responsibility for health and safety and delegating is also an important part of being an effective leader.

Environmental, health and safety (EHS) and management as a conduit for change

The International Organization for Standardization (ISO) have published standards to help organisations manage their environmental aspects (hazards) and health and safety risks. You will probably be familiar with these standards; the environmental standard is ISO 14001:2015 and the health and safety standard is ISO 45001:2018 (previously OHSAS 18001). Your organisation may very well be certified against one or both of these standards. By following these standards, organisations are showing their commitment to protect the environment and the health and safety of their workers and others who visit their site. One of the clauses of a management system relates to improvement (including continual improvement). Organisations should be striving continuously to improve their own performance and influence change/improvement within other organisations where possible.

Management systems encourage change through (continuous) improvement

One way of influencing other organisations, is via the supply chain. Organisation with mature, well managed EHS management systems can insist that these higher standards are cascaded down into their supply chains. As organisations adopt higher EHS standards they will very often require the same standards from other organisations within their supply chains. Many organisations will no longer deal with businesses who cannot evidence how they manage their EHS issues. This can go both ways within a supply chain eg, not purchasing from companies with poor EHS standards as well as not selling their products to them. Very often supply-chain audits are carried out before contracts are signed to ensure that businesses are actually doing what they say they are doing. The possible loss of business is a massive driver for organisations to change their health and safety culture and standards.

Larger organisations will very often publish details about their Corporate Social Responsibility (CSR). These organisations will want to be seen as exemplars within their industry and will go beyond the minimum legal standards. This in turn could have an effect on competitors. The competitor will not want to be seen as less ethical than the competition and will, therefore, raise their own standards. This again can loop around to influence their own supply chains.

Some organisations, however, may not need the threat of lost business to change; some companies will change for ethical reasons; they want to be seen to be doing the right thing. This is very important to many businesses, especially with the influence of the media, social media in particular. It only takes one story about unethical trading to 'go viral' to ruin the reputation of a business.

Blame culture, no name no blame and just culture

Blame culture

It is likely you will have encountered the term 'blame culture' which should be self-explanatory. A blame culture is the default culture due to human beings' inherent need to put blame outside of ourselves.

An organisation that has a blame culture seeks to find out who is responsible, then to attribute blame. This could lead to punishment, possibly disciplinary action, maybe dismissal, perhaps some retraining and certainly the blame for the incident or accident being placed on an individual or group. You may consider this fair or not, but if the focus is on blaming people this culture will not encourage the sharing of information on actions that led to errors; people do not want to be blamed! In this culture, people are unlikely to share this knowledge or report incidents as they are afraid of recriminations; additionally, there will be a lack of organisational learning.

It is, therefore, unlikely that a 'blame culture' is going to lead to long-term improvement of health and safety. Perhaps, because blaming people often seems to provide an easy way to show that 'justice has been done', and is certainly less complex and time consuming than properly investigating the issue, reviewing and changing processes and procedures; this is why 'blame culture' seems so prolific.

As mentioned earlier, a blame culture is a default 'setting'. Workers within an organisation can believe that their organisation has a blame culture (default setting) when, in fact, this is not the case. However, just the belief in an organisational blame culture can be enough to stop workers reporting accidents and near misses. It is, therefore, important that health and safety leaders demonstrate a commitment to an alternative culture to change the organisation's default setting of blame culture.

ACTIVITY

Why do you think a blame culture may develop within an organisation?

What might some indicators be and how would you address them?

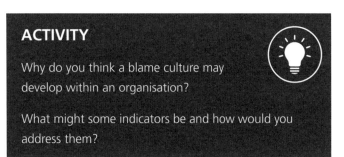

No name, no blame

The opposite of the blame culture is unsurprisingly a 'no-blame culture'.

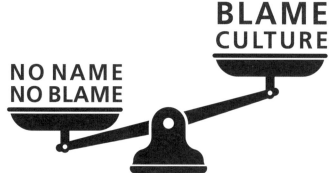

This culture is built on the belief that blame is not the issue. If a problem occurs, it is investigated to try and find out why it happened. Workers are encouraged to speak openly about problems and mistakes. The workforce and managers are empowered to be honest and open; the most vital consideration is making things work properly and preventing mistakes from happening again. However the issue with no name, no blame is that nobody is held accountable for their actions.

Just culture

A just culture takes the no name no blame idea one stage further to a 'just, no blame culture' or 'just culture'. A just culture is the balancing point between a blame culture and a no name no blame culture.

Here, blame would only be attributed, when somebody has been reckless and taken unnecessary and unacceptable risks. An effective health and safety leader will be required to show support for workers when things genuinely go wrong. This will encourage the reporting of incidents without fear of blame. This in turn will mean the organisation will benefit from understanding why accidents or incidents occurred and how to take appropriate action to prevent them happening again.

However, in a just culture leaders must also recognise that they must give recognition for safe behaviour. They must also appreciate that accountability must be delivered in a fair and consistent manner, no matter what level the individual is at within the organisation. Consistent accountability and recognition are two things that many organisations do badly.

Three-aspect approach to health and safety culture

The diagram below is from the HSE's Research Report 367[17] shows the three aspect approach to Health and Safety Culture. Based on Cooper's Theory 2000. This illustrates that an organisations safety culture will depend on three aspects: psychological, behavioural and situational (as shown below). The connecting arrows shows that the three aspects are interrelated and not stand alone elements.

Psychological aspects are about how people feel within the organisation's and why. This may have more to do with the workforce's perceptions of how the organisation may ensure a safe and secure environment. It will also include individuals' attitudes about the organisation, each other, the work they do, the environment in which they work, as well as their own beliefs and values built over time. Attitude affects behaviour.

Behavioural aspects, as in how people (workforce, management, leaders) act with regard to health and safety within the workplace; it also takes account of the impact that their behaviour has on the overall safety culture of the organisation.

Situational aspects comprises the organisation's own

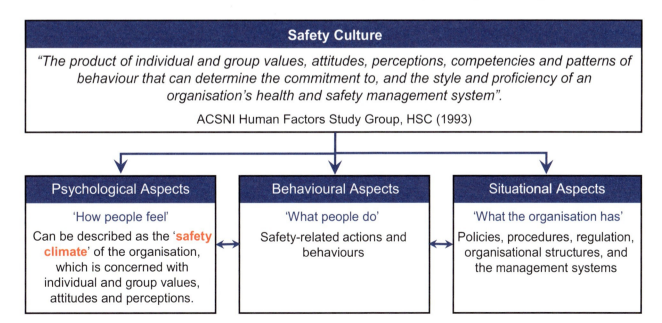

Source: A review of safety culture and safety climate literature for the development of the safety culture inspection toolkit, HSE 2005, Research Report 367 [17]

Element 1 **The foundations of health and safety leadership**

processes, rules, regulations and procedures as well as how it is set up and what the structure looks like. This would determine the 'messages' being communicated to the wider workforce about the organisation's attitude towards health and safety.

These three factors together form the basis of the safety culture of an organisation. If individual members or groups within the workforce feel there is a lack of interest in following safety procedures, it could lead to the perception of a poor safety culture; this in turn could promote negative behaviour. It is, therefore, vital for an effective health and safety leader to understand the importance of monitoring and maintaining the organisational aspects of the culture. The leader will also need to keep a close eye on workforce attitudes by engaging in a continuous 'conversation' with those involved.

Levels of maturity in health and safety culture

It is important for anyone involved in health and safety leadership to be aware of where their organisation is positioned with regard to a health and safety culture. As with any sort of strategy it is essential to know 'where you are now' so that planning will be effective for improvement and growth. The following characteristics can be used to illustrate and explain the different stages of maturity an organisation may travel through on the journey from Ad-Hoc to Excellence.

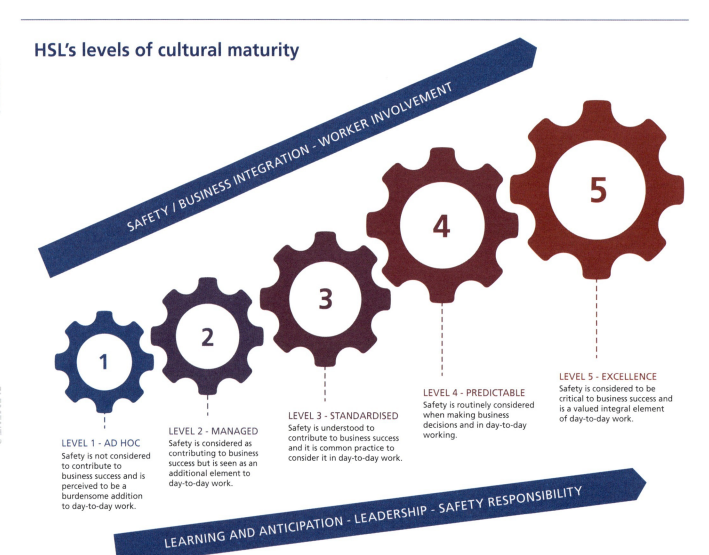

HSL's levels of cultural maturity

SAFETY / BUSINESS INTEGRATION - WORKER INVOLVEMENT

LEARNING AND ANTICIPATION - LEADERSHIP - SAFETY RESPONSIBILITY

LEVEL 1 - AD HOC
Safety is not considered to contribute to business success and is perceived to be a burdensome addition to day-to-day work.

LEVEL 2 - MANAGED
Safety is considered as contributing to business success but is seen as an additional element to day-to-day work.

LEVEL 3 - STANDARDISED
Safety is understood to contribute to business success and it is common practice to consider it in day-to-day work.

LEVEL 4 - PREDICTABLE
Safety is routinely considered when making business decisions and in day-to-day working.

LEVEL 5 - EXCELLENCE
Safety is considered to be critical to business success and is a valued integral element of day-to-day work.

Element 1 The foundations of health and safety leadership

Level 1: Ad Hoc

- Safety is not considered to contribute to business success and is perceived to be a burdensome addition to day-to-day work.

- Safety is seen as the responsibility of the health and safety department by everybody in the organisation.

- Senior leaders are willing to compromise safety if it appears to be a barrier to productivity and where workers have little interest in safety.

- Accidents are seen as unavoidable and if investigations are undertaken the focus is on who is to blame.

Level 2: Managed

- Safety is recognised as contributing to business success but is seen as an additional element of day-to-day working.

- Managers recognise that they have a role to play in safety but the health and safety department take the lead.

- Individuals recognise that they have responsibility for their own health and safety and are occasionally consulted about health and safety.

- Accidents are seen as avoidable and investigations are undertaken but are limited in scope, response or learning.

- Leading indicators for safety are not considered.

Level 3: Standardised

- Safety is understood to contribute to business success and it is common practice to consider it in day-to-day work.

- Everybody recognises that they contribute to health and safety but the health and safety department is regarded as the lead and workers tend to look out for themselves and their immediate colleagues.

- Senior leaders are committed to health and safety but this commitment is not always realised at all levels of the organisation.

- Workers are willing to take part in consultation but this tends to be reactive and piecemeal.

- There is an acknowledgement that organisational factors can contribute to accidents and there is some learning from investigations.

- A limited range of leading indicators are monitored to identify potential safety issues.

Level 4: Predictable

- Safety is routinely considered when making business decisions and in day-to-day working.

- Everybody recognises that they are responsible not only for their own safety but also the safety of their colleagues throughout the organisation.

- There is a clear commitment to health and safety by leaders at every level.

- Engagement with workers is proactive and meaningful.

- Lessons are learnt from both accident and near miss investigations.

- There are a good range of leading indicators that are regularly monitored to identify health and safety issues.

Level 5: Excellent

- Safety is considered to be critical to business success and is a valued, integral element of day-to-day work activities.

- Everybody within the organisation recognises that they are responsible for safety.

- There is routine, visible senior leadership and strong partnership working with all levels within the organisation.

- Accident and near miss investigations consider the full range of root causes and the emphasis is learning from accidents and near misses.

- The organisation actively exploits a wide variety of information to anticipate potential safety issues.

It should be noted, however, that there could be several different levels of cultural maturity across an organisation. For example, an organisation that has multiple sites or operates in different locations around the world.

1.4

ACTIVITY

From the characteristics we have just looked at, where do think your own organisation sits within these levels?

What sort of evidence would you present to support your argument?

Leading and lagging indicators of health and safety culture

KEY TERMS

Indicators (leading and lagging)

Measurements taken to assess safety performance and determine what needs to be done to improve the safety culture of an organisation.

Leading indicators

Leading indicators are proactive; they aim to prevent adverse events before they happen.

Lagging indicators

Lagging indicators are reactive; they aim to measure the effectiveness of safety management systems after events have occurred.

Planned maintenance programmes is an example of a leading indicator

It is important for a health and safety leader to understand that there is a range of indicators that can be used to help them manage health and safety. Leading indicators can help to improve safety culture by preventing unwanted events from happening. By having a good range of leading indicators this will show workers and other relevant stakeholders that the organisation is taking health and safety seriously. Lagging indicators are useful in identifying trends but, as they measure past events (normally failures), are not particularly useful when trying to prevent unwanted events from happening.

Some of the indicators you can use include:

Leading indicators (note, it is important to bear in mind not just the quantity of these metrics, but also the quality eg, how competence is assessed following training):

- results of safety campaigns;
- safety training for the workforce;
- number of toolbox talks;
- risk assessments;
- outcomes from health and safety committees/worker involvement in health and safety;
- lessons learnt databases;
- job safety analyses;
- leadership site visits/number of walkabouts;
- review of procedures (completed on time and have involved relevant workers);
- suggestion programmes and evidence of changes made;
- training opportunities, assessments and feedback;
- number of production down-times (if related to safety);
- safety audits; and
- planned maintenance programmes for the workplace and work equipment/machinery.

Lagging indicators:

- number of fatalities;
- number of days lost through ill-health or workplace injuries;
- number and types of ill-health and injuries;
- how often accidents may happen;
- number of prosecutions or civil actions;
- number of enforcement notices issued by regulators; and
- number of reportable incidents.

Measuring the 'right' things

As mentioned in the last section, understanding where an organisation is on the scale of health and safety cultural maturity is important for any leader to make progress. For this to happen the organisation must carry out measurements and monitoring of procedures and processes. However, we should not forget these must be the 'right' procedures and processes to have any real value. It is surprising but all too common for organisations to measure things which are easy to find or show things in a favourable light that is not at all useful for the leader who really wants to create an effective health and safety culture.

A well-used model in measuring risk is The James Reason Swiss Cheese Failure Model. The following is a brief explanation of how the model works.

- Reason compares defensive layers to several layers of Swiss cheese.
- Each layer of 'cheese' is a defence against a hazard being realised (mistakes and failures).
- Each defence has holes in it.
- Things do go wrong from time to time; so something breaking through one of the holes is not too much of a problem. We cope with minor failures easily, it's part of normal routine. We fix these errors and then move on.
- Things tend to go wrong when holes align through all of the layers. This shows us that all risk control systems have failed and there will be a major failure/the hazard is realised.

1.4

The following is an example of how the holes align easily due to the limited amount of checking which will cause a failure.

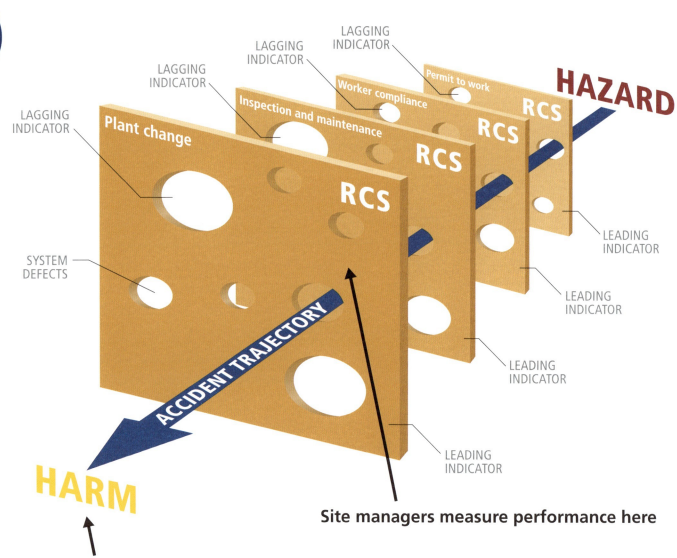

KEY:

RCS - Risk Control System

The next diagram shows the same layers but with more checking in place. By carrying out the extra checks we make it more difficult for the holes to align; this will cut down on the chances of the hazard being realised.

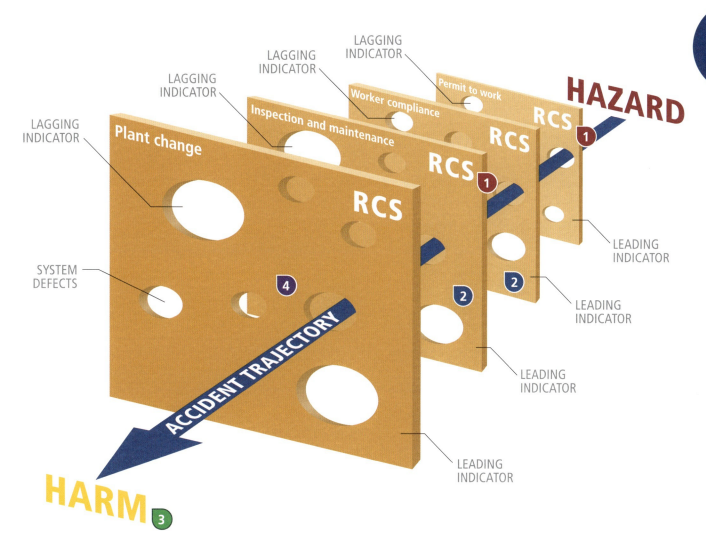

KEY:

① by ensuring these actions take place; and

② measuring success or failure here;

③ we are having an effect here; and

④ having less reliance here.

Who uses it? The Swiss Cheese Model has been used extensively in risk management, health care, aviation, and engineering. It is very useful as a method for explaining the concept of cumulative effects.

Models like this are essential tools in the toolkit of the effective health and safety leader. As indeed is learning from other organisational practices and benchmarking best practice from wherever you can find it. The industry or sector from which this best practice comes is often irrelevant; with slight modification a process, procedure or working practice can be rewritten to fit the needs of an organisation. It is good leadership that recognises promotes and encourages a root and branch approach to health and safety culture.

High Reliability Organisations (HROs)

> **KEY TERMS**
>
> *High Reliability Organisation (HRO)*
>
> This is an organisation that is able to manage and sustain, almost error-free, performance despite operating in hazardous conditions where the consequences of errors could be catastrophic.[18]

HROs were first developed in the following sectors:

- power grid dispatching centres;
- air traffic control systems;
- nuclear power plants;
- wildfire fire-fighters;
- aircraft operations; and
- accident investigation teams.

HROs, as we saw from the 'Key Term' definition, have capacity to maintain or regain a stable state which is something all organisations should aspire to. HRO's generally have the following characteristics:

Containment of unexpected (emergency) events

HROs will generally:

- invest heavily in technical expertise within their organisation. They will value those with such expertise and listen to and follow their advice/instructions;
- allow their experts to make important safety-related decisions in emergencies; during normal operating conditions there is a clear hierarchical structure and an understanding of who does what;
- invest in training for workers at all levels to ensure that the organisation has the right levels of competence throughout the organisation; and
- will ensure that they have back-up/redundancy systems in place and have emergency plans in place for unexpected events.

Just culture

A just culture is one where accountability and recognition are dealt with consistently throughout the organisation.

Mindful leadership

Much of this content is discussed later in this book. However, HROs generally will have leaders who are:

- visible and actively engage with the workforce;
- prepared to receive bottom-up communications which have bad news; they will ensure that there are communication channels available to allow this type of reporting;
- able to ensure that sufficient resources are made available for all operations; whether this be people or equipment;
- able to balance profits with safety ie, by encouraging all staff to follow procedures and not cut corners; and
- involved in proactively commissioning audits to identify problems in systems; this can be in response to incidents that occur in other similar industries.

Element 1 **The foundations of health and safety leadership**

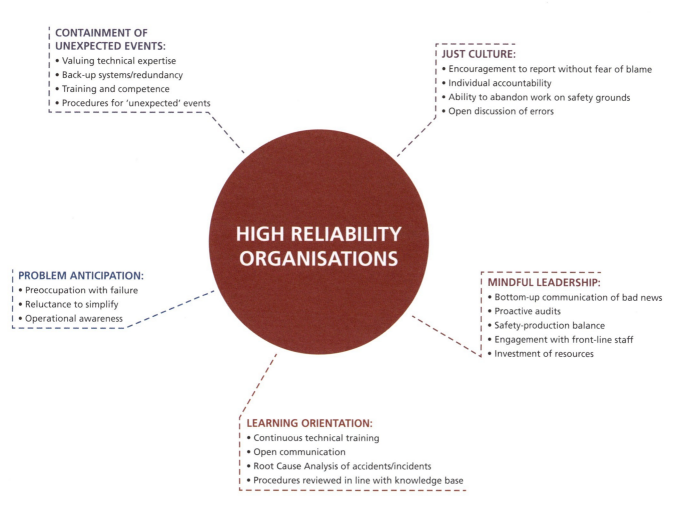

Learning orientation

HROs will general have systems in place which allow for:

- continuous technical training;
- systematic analysis of incidents to identify their root causes and accident types or trends within the organisation;
- open communication of accident investigation outcomes; and
- updating procedures in line with the organisational knowledge base.

Problem anticipation

HROs will also generally be able to anticipate potential failures by:

- engaging with front line workers in order to obtain 'the bigger picture' of operations (sensitivity to operations);
- attentiveness to minor or what may appear as trivial signals that may indicate potential problem areas within the organisation and use incidents and near misses as indicators of a system's 'health' (preoccupation with failure); and
- carry out systematic collection and analysis of all warning signals, no matter how trivial they may appear to be, and avoid making assumptions regarding the nature of failures. Explanations regarding the causes of incidents tend to be systemic rather than focusing on individual, 'blame the operator' justifications (reluctance to simplify).

Over reliance on technology

One of the draw backs of HROs is their over reliance on technology to avoid unexpected events. Generally these organisations (as we saw earlier) tend to maintain back-up and redundancy systems to help manage these events.

The problem with this is that there is the possibility of relying too much on 'machinery' and ignoring the human inputs. There is also the possibility that machinery/technology will reduce the number of workers required on site; this could include those with technical expertise. We sometimes put too much faith in technology always being correct and always working.

Element 1 The foundations of health and safety leadership

ACTIVITY

Do you recognise any of the HRO characteristics within your own organisation?

How close do you feel you are to this type of health and safety culture?

How would you, as a leader, influence the organisation to move in this direction?

Element 1 references / further reading

References

1 What is leadership, Chartered Institute of Personnel and Development (CIPD) https://www.cipd.co.uk/knowledge/strategy/leadership/factsheet

2 Why leadership is important, HSE http://www.hse.gov.uk/leadership/whyleadership.htm

3 Leadership failure case study, HSE http://www.hse.gov.uk/leadership/casestudies-failures.htm

4 Leadership success case study, HSE http://www.hse.gov.uk/leadership/casestudies.htm

5 Managing for health and safety, HSE Books http://www.hse.gov.uk/pubns/priced/hsg65.pdf

6 Risk assessment, A brief guide to controlling risks in the workplace, INDG163, HSE Books, http://www.hse.gov.uk/pubns/indg163.pdf

7 Section 37 prosecution https://www.shponline.co.uk/880k-fine-horrific-machinery-death/

8 Gross negligence manslaughter case https://www.shponline.co.uk/golf-company-director-jailed-lake-death/

9 Corporate Manslaughter case (Cotswold Geotech) https://www.healthandsafetyatwork.com/cotswold-geotech-guilty

10 Corporate Manslaughter case (Baldwins Crane Hire) https://www.healthandsafetyatwork.com/corporate-killing/baldwins-crane-hire-easton

11 and 12 The Health and Safety Offences and Corporate Manslaughter sentencing guidelines https://www.sentencingcouncil.org.uk/wp-content/uploads/HS-offences-definitive-guideline-FINAL-web.pdf

13 Scottish Sentencing Council https://www.scottishsentencingcouncil.org.uk/about-sentencing/sentencing-factors/

14 Leading health and safety at work, IoD and HSE http://www.hse.gov.uk/pubns/indg417.pdf

15 and 16 HSE Human Factors Briefing Note No. 7, Safety Culture http://www.hse.gov.uk/humanfactors/topics/07culture.pdf

17 A review of safety culture and safety climate literature for the development of the safety culture inspection toolkit, HSE 2005, Research Report 367 http://www.hse.gov.uk/research/rrpdf/rr367.pdf

18 High reliability organisations, a review of the literature, HSE, 2011, Research Report RR899 http://www.hse.gov.uk/research/rrpdf/rr899.pdf

Further reading

Common topic 4: Safety culture, HSE
http://www.hse.gov.uk/foi/internalops/fod/inspect/mast/safetychecklist.pdf

Involving your workforce in health and safety, Guidance for all workplaces
http://www.hse.gov.uk/pUbns/priced/hsg263.pdf

Leadership and worker involvement toolkit, Good health and safety leadership
http://www.hse.gov.uk/construction/lwit/assets/downloads/good-health-safety-leadership.pdf

Towards a model of safety culture, M.D. Cooper Ph.D., 2000
http://www.behavioral-safety.com/articles/Towards_a_model_of_safety_culture.pdf

Notes

Human failure and decision making

This chapter will explore how human failure can impact the health and safety culture of an organisation. We will look at HSE's 'Make it happen' model and how it can illustrate the influences on health and safety behaviours within an organisation. The chapter will then look how we all use mental short cuts, perception biases, habits and beliefs to influence our decision-making process.

Learning outcomes

- Understand how human failure can impact on health and safety culture and how the 'Make it happen' model can help to change behaviours

- Recognise how mental short cuts, perception biases, habits and beliefs can influence the decision-making process.

2.1 Understanding how human failure can impact on health and safety culture and how the 'Make it Happen' model can help to change behaviours

In this section we are going to examine the relationship between human failure and decision making and how human failure impacts safety culture.

> **KEY TERMS**
>
> *Error:* an unintentional action or decision.
>
> *Violation:* an intentional failure or deliberately doing the wrong thing.

The following illustration is from the HSE's publication 'Reducing error and influencing behaviour (HSG48)' and illustrates the various types of human failures. These are broken down between errors and violations and we will look at each of these in more detail shortly.

```
HUMAN FAILURES
├── ERRORS
│   ├── SKILL-BASED ERRORS
│   │   ├── LAPSES OF MEMORY
│   │   └── SLIPS OF ACTION
│   └── MISTAKES
│       ├── RULE-BASED MISTAKES
│       └── KNOWLEDGE-BASED MISTAKES
└── VIOLATIONS
    ├── ROUTINE
    ├── SITUATIONAL
    └── EXCEPTIONAL
```

Figure 1 taken from HSG48[1], Reducing error and influencing behaviour

As we can see errors are broken down into 'skill-based errors' and 'mistakes'.

Element 2 **Human failure and decision making**

Errors

Skill-based errors

Errors usually occur in very familiar tasks where we do not need to pay much attention to what we are doing. One of the most common example of a skill-based activity is driving a car. If a slip of action or a lapse of memory occurs, even momentarily, the consequences can be devastating. Slips and lapses can happen even to well-trained, experienced individuals.

Skilled-based errors are broken down into 'slips of action' and 'lapses of memory'.

Slips of action

These are unintentional failures to carry out all actions of a task, in other words, unplanned actions. Some examples of slips of action are:

- performing an action either too soon or too late in a procedure;
- forgetting to perform one or more steps in a procedure;
- carrying out the action in the wrong direction eg, turning a piece of machinery to a higher speed instead of turning it off;
- performing the right activity but on the wrong piece of equipment (eg, flicking a switch on or off but not on the right piece of equipment); or
- carrying out the wrong check but on the right piece of equipment (eg, checking a dial but recording the wrong information).

Lapses of memory

Again these are unintentional. A lapse means that you will forget to carry out an action in an activity; or forgetting where you are in a particular process meaning you could do the right thing but at the wrong time.

You can minimise lapses of memory by:

- minimising distractions eg, try to stop workers from talking to each other while performing an activity;
- providing reminders of the steps involved in the activity eg, providing a ticklist that can be completed after each stage of an activity;
- designing tasks in a better way eg, so that the operator does not need to leave their workstation half-way through an activity.

Element 2 **Human failure and decision making**

Mistakes

Mistakes happen when you think that you are doing the right thing but it is actually wrong. Mistakes are a more complex form of errors.

Mistakes are broken down between 'rule-based mistakes' and 'knowledge-based mistakes'.

Rule-based mistakes

Your behaviour is based on remembered rules or familiar procedures. There is a strong inclination to use the familiar even when this may be wrong or not the most efficient way of dealing with the situation. An example of a rule-based mistake is where a tanker driver ignores high level alarms when filling a tank because he knows how long the tank takes to fill as he has done it many times before. However, on this occasion he does not realise that the diameter of the pipe entering the tank had been enlarged meaning that the tank would fill quicker. The result being that the tank being filled overfills and overflows.

Knowledge-based mistakes

These mistakes tend to happen when you are in unfamiliar situations and there are no 'tried and tested' rules to rely upon. You will tend to rely on knowledge of similar situations to try to reach a solution for the unfamiliar situation. We make an incorrect decision due to not having all the information we need; or we simplify the information available to us and move too quickly to a decision without considering all options. Sometimes these errors occur at work because an individual has to deal with a situation that is beyond their level of understanding.

An example of a knowledge-based mistake is when we try to amend a process by relying on information that we did not know was out of date or from past experiences.

Violations

The HSE's publication 'Reducing error and influencing behaviour' (HSG48) refers to violations as deliberate deviations from rules, procedures and instructions designed for safety and efficiency of a system.

Slips and lapses may be attributed to human error or simply just being human and making mistakes as we all do. Violations are a deliberate attempt to avoid or ignore procedures and instructions that have been designed to safeguard people and property. The reasons for violation of these processes and deliberately doing the wrong thing may be many and varied. They will however, according to the HSE, fall into one of three categories; routine, situational or exceptional. The report 'Improving compliance with safety procedures, reducing industrial violations'[2] outlines practical strategies for reducing the potential for violations, as well as highlighting some significant and devastating examples of violations and their consequences.

A *routine violation* is where breaking the rules has become a normal way of working within the workforce. This can be due to several reasons including:

- cutting corners to save time;
- the workforce may feel that the rules are to prescriptive;
- if carried on for a long period of time, the workforce may feel that the rules no longer apply;
- if leadership does not enforce rules the workforce will continue to ignore them; and
- new workers entering the workforce may not realise that routine violations are the norm; they may not realise that rules apply.

A **situational violation** occurs in response to situational factors, including excessive time pressure, workplace design, extreme weather conditions and inadequate or inappropriate equipment. When confronted with an unexpected or inappropriate situation, workers may believe that the normal rule is no longer safe, or that it will not achieve the desired outcome, and so they decide to violate that rule. Situational violations generally occur as a one-off, unless the situation triggering the violation is not corrected, in which case the violation may become routine over time.

An **exceptional violation** is a fairly rare occurrence and happens in abnormal and emergency situations. This type of violation transpires when something is going wrong and workers believe that they must break the rules even though they know this is a risk. Workers choose to violate the rule believing that they will achieve the desired outcome.

2.1

The HSE's 'Make it Happen' model

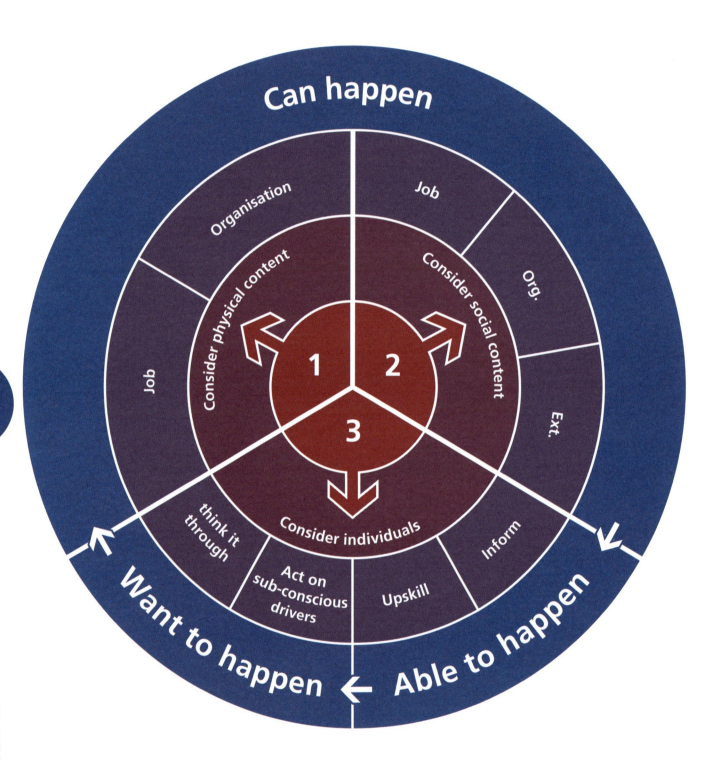

Element 2 **Human failure and decision making**

The Health and Safety Executive's agency Health and Safety Laboratory (HSL) developed a 'Make it Happen' model for health and safety based on the HSL's approach to behaviour change. The model is based upon the evidence base for behaviour change. It helps us to identify and understand the myriad of influences that are driving key health and safety behaviours/issues (in both management and workforce) and then to identify solutions/interventions that could be developed to address these behaviours/issues.

Behaviour change within the workplace requires an approach that tackles the multiple influences on behaviour from both the work context as well as the individual. These factors as captured by the model include:

- Factors arising from the work context (physical and social environment) that either enable or act as barriers to safe behaviour. Addressing these factors means that safe behaviour 'can happen'.

- Individual factors that influence behaviour concerning an individual's capability ie, their knowledge and skills (technical and interpersonal). Improving these means that behaviour change is 'able to happen'.

- Addressing influences that operate at a deliberate (conscious decision making) or 'automatic' (bias, habit) level. Addressing these means that your workforce will 'want' behaviour change 'to happen'.

Can it happen?

Are your jobs well designed? Do you have a genuinely supportive health and safety culture? Are you confident that your senior leaders possess the right skills to act as enablers for safe/healthy behaviour? Is safety always the priority for your organisation, even when the business is under pressure?

Able to happen?

Do your workers have the right health and safety knowledge and skills? Is training really making a difference or is it merely regarded as a 'box-ticking' exercise? Would workers express the same views on your health and safety culture to both a manager and a colleague?

Do we want it to happen?

Is your workforce motivated and committed to creating a better health and safety culture? What are the influences on health and safety decision making that operate at a deliberate (conscious decision making) or 'automatic' (bias, habit) level?

An effective health and safety leader would need to understand how essential it is to monitor their own organisation for signs of possible problems with attitudes or behaviours towards health and safety. This may arise anywhere within the organisation from front line workers to senior management. Ensuring an appropriate level of excellence and buy-in is a continuous process and requires a creative approach.

Providing support and recognition (health and safety leadership value 3)

People recognise when they are valued, and they should be provided with a good idea of their value to the organisation. If workers are treated as valued team members, not as numbers, they will respond positively. When a leader shows genuine interest in supporting others in the workforce there is a positive effect.

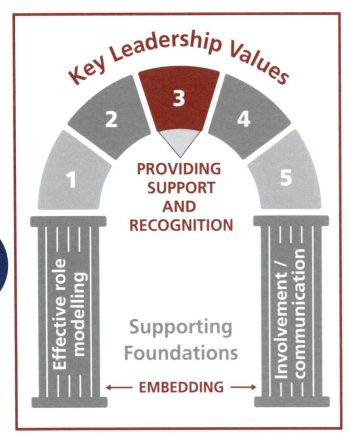

Training and development are key to ensuring workers have the right tools to carry out the job. Identifying what is needed requires a continuing dialogue. As a leader you should be ensuring that advice and guidance concerning best practice in health and safety is readily available to anyone who looks for it. Importantly, this advice and guidance should be assessed to ensure the appropriate language is used for the different audiences as well as accessibility. There is little point in distributing training or guidance if the users have difficulty finding or using it. This also causes frustration and may lead to disengagement and scepticism from those with which you are trying to engage.

Recognising and rewarding the efforts made by individuals and teams will help provide motivation and continued efforts. Rewards can come in many shapes and sizes aside from financial, which of course from a resourcing perspective are often the most difficult to provide.

As discussed elsewhere people are motivated by a wide variety of things. Singling people out for special recognition can be very motivating. Providing extra training opportunities for those who aspire to improve their skills can prove highly effective in motivation and building strong long term relationships. Ensuring that resources are provided where and when needed fairly and without prejudice will show that support is real and ongoing, thus building trust based on fairness.

ASSESSMENT ACTIVITY 3

Please refer to the document Unit HSL1, guidance and information for candidates and internal assessors.

You should now complete task
L3: Providing support and recognition.

Decision-making processes, mental shortcuts, perception biases and habits.

The differences between 'Automatic' and 'Reflective' decision making.

Automatic and reflective decision making

As we have seen when we explored the 'Make it happen' model, some decision-making processes will have an influence on behaviour. We will now explore different types of decision making in more detail.

Understanding the differences between Automatic and Reflective decision making can start with how you make decisions. While there are many and varied influences and reasons behind why someone chooses to do what they do, let us start with a couple of basics.

For example, how might you decide which area to live in, which property to live in, or which career you might choose? For most people, these are important decisions, requiring care and attention and unhurried, considered responses. You would probably have a gut feeling about which to choose, however you would still, most likely, carry out research, investigate options, compare and contrast as much information as you can, as well as seeking other people's views so that you can arrive at a rational decision based on a thorough investigation and a period of reflection. Hence a 'reflective' decision-making process.

It is unlikely that you would adopt a similar position about which chocolate bar you might buy, which TV programme you will watch or which seat to occupy on a train. While carrying out detailed research and building a list of strengths, weaknesses, pros and cons about houses and careers is no doubt a sensible and appropriate response. Doing the same for confectionary, a 30 minute train ride or any number of other seemingly unimportant, but nonetheless necessary daily decisions, would mean we probably would never decide on anything, as well as wasting huge amounts of time and achieving very little. This is why we often rely to a considerable extent on 'automatic' decision making for these tasks.

This method enables us to make quick decisions, based on not much information but supplemented by a variety of 'shortcuts' you have developed during your life. Marketers know this very well and use it with extraordinary effectiveness to ensure we choose their particular product or service over those of the competition without us ever really knowing why.

These two methods of making decisions are present in all of us. Psychologist Daniel Kahneman refers to these two systems in the mind as System 1 and System 2.

System 1 is the automatic, rapid almost unconscious way of thinking which is efficient, requires little or no effort or attention, but is prone to slip-ups and mistakes.

System 2 is reflective and requires effort and attention, it is a slower, more controlled way of thinking. It also has the capability to moderate the instincts present in System 1.

These two systems are examined further in Kahneman's book 'Thinking Fast and Slow'.

Our brain can make split-second decisions without any effort on our part at all and we have no voluntary control over this aspect of our brain. This system is helpful in certain situations, but it can also get us into trouble because it can be emotional. System 1 is biased to believe and confirm. It also focuses on existing evidence and ignores lacking evidence. Kahneman calls this "what you see is all there is".

The graphic opposite shows Kahneman's framework for fast and slow thinking.

2.2

	SYSTEM 1	SYSTEM 2
CHARACTERISTICS	Fast Effortless Unconscious Triggers emotions Associative Looks for patterns Looks for causation Creates stories to explain events	Slow Effortful Conscious Logical Deliberative Can handle abstract concepts
ADVANTAGES	Speed of response in a crisis Easy completion of routine or repetitive tasks Creativity through associations, so is good for expansive thinking	Allows reflection and consideration of the "bigger picture", options, pros and cons, consequences Can handle logic, maths, statistics Good for reductive thinking
DISADVANTAGES	Jumps to conclusions Unhelpful emotional responses Can make errors that are not detected and corrected, such as wrong assumptions, poor judgements, false casual links	Slow, so requires time Requires effort and energy, which can lead to decision fatigue

Our attention span has a limited capacity and the way in which we act reflects this. For example, when overtaking a lorry on a two-lane road, adult passengers will generally stop talking as they do not want to distract the driver during such a crucial manoeuvre.

When instructed to focus on one task it can make people 'blind' to other activities going on in the same area. Christopher Chabris and Daniel Simons illustrate this in the book 'The Invisible Gorilla'. They produced a short video of two teams playing basketball; one team wearing white tops and the other wearing black tops. The instruction at the beginning of the video is to count the number of passes made by the team wearing the white tops (so totally discounting the team in black tops). At the end of the video you are asked 'how many passes' and the next question is 'did you see the gorilla?'. Over half of the people who watch the video for the first time miss the gorilla, although it stays in the video for roughly 10 seconds.

We are using System 1 thinking when carrying out this observational task; however, to be able to 'see the gorilla' we need to be able to notice unexpected stimuli in a situation. When we cannot concentrate on all stimuli we become temporarily blind to the additional stimuli to the observational task and ignore them.

Mental shortcuts can help to move through the mass of information we hold when making decisions

Reliable mental shortcuts

Some estimates suggest that a person can make up to 32,000 decisions in a single day, many of which we do not even know we are making. It is no surprise that we have developed a range of mental shortcuts to help (or hinder) the process of making decisions. In psychology, the term 'heuristics' refer to these simple rules that people often use to form judgments and make decisions. They are 'mental shortcuts' that "enable a person to discover or learn something for themselves/ proceed to a solution by trial and error or by rules that are only loosely defined." (Oxford Dictionary of English).

Three of the most important shortcuts used when evaluating risk are 'availability', 'representativeness' and 'anchoring and adjustment'.

Where organisational risks are well known, heuristics can be effective when estimating the level of risk. The draw back to this is that we can sometimes place too much belief in judgements reached by using heuristics. However, where the risk is not so well know we can apply biases which may mean we make incorrect assumptions about the risk.

Here are some of the more common mental shortcuts used in decision making.

Anchoring

The anchoring shortcut (or rule of thumb) describes the common human tendency to rely too heavily on the first piece of information offered (the anchor) when making decisions. Once the anchor is set, decisions are then made by adjusting around the initial anchor, regardless of the legitimacy of the actual anchor.

If you think how most of us decide if a price is 'right' we need an initial figure to focus on to 'help' make that decision. If we are told the recommended retail price is £600 and we think that is too high, we are far more likely to buy if we are offered the item at £150, despite the fact it was never ever worth £600 and in fact should be £100! We 'anchor' to a number and this becomes part of the decision-making process.

In a health and safety scenario anchoring may act as a reference point that connects a historical event with the present and uses past experiences to influence decisions. Maybe if a supervisor was involved in a serious forklift truck incident at some stage in the past, further discussion of this topic may trigger an 'anchoring' response based on this past experience. This may result in either a raised level of awareness and knowledge, or conversely, perhaps a degree of over-sensitivity and a reluctance to engage.

The effective health and safety leader will need to understand the situation and consider whether a more sensitive line of enquiry would be better rather than using normal questioning techniques.

Mental shortcuts used for estimating the outcome of an event based on information we can easily recall

Availability

Recalling some things more easily than other things is normal for most people. Availability shortcuts assist in estimating how likely something is to happen based on information that we can easily recall. People make judgments about the likelihood of an event or situation based on how easily an example, instance or case comes to mind.

The availability heuristic can be helpful when we are faced with a choice but we do not have the time to investigate before making our final choice. The availability heuristic will help you to come to an immediate decision. However, it is important to understand that this could lead to incorrect decisions being made.

For example, we may hear a traffic update at the same time each day that features a particular motorway section. Based on this we might consider this to be a particularly troubling route; this may not be the case, it just happens to be the one we know about. Similarly, in the workplace, if we are exposed to several incidents that took place in a specific area, we may decide that this is a particularly difficult area and requires special consideration. This may be right, but it may also be because we recall more about this area, maybe because we know someone well who works there, or it is more on our 'radar' than other departments.

The effective leader will understand that these factors require consideration in order to make rational decisions.

Representativeness

This is a type of mental shortcut that enables quick decision making based on previous experience when faced with uncertainty. The representativeness heuristic is simply described as assessing the similarity of objects or events and organising them based around the category prototype (eg, like goes with like and causes and effects should resemble each other).

The representativeness heuristic is, therefore, used when making judgments about the probability that object, or event A, belongs to class B by looking at the degree to which A resembles B.

When people rely on representativeness to make judgments, they are likely to judge wrongly because the fact that something is more representative does not actually make it more likely.

This mental shortcut may provide quick decisions but will these be the right decisions? We may be basing them on fallacies, which is to say we may be pulling up examples from the past to represent the challenge we are facing; but we may not really understand that these situations are different and require more information to be useful.

The next time you are trying to make a decision, consider the way in which the representative heuristic might play a role in your thinking.

A good example of representativeness is called the 'gambler's fallacy' which is where someone believes that runs of good and bad luck occur. So, if a coin toss turns up heads multiple times in a row, people think that 'tails' is a more likely occurrence in the next toss. They think that this will even things out, even though the opposite may happen and that heads will continue the winning streak. People think this, despite the fact that each toss of the coin is a totally independent event and not connected to the one before or after it.

The 'gambler's fallacy'

Media influence

It is all too easy for our decisions to be irrationally based on media influence. Alongside the conventional broadcast and print media, social media has now taken its place with exceptional powers of persuasion and the much discussed 'fake news' elements. If one of our favourite celebrities appears on the television selling Brand A, we tend to immediately believe this has to be good; we often forget that the celebrity in question has been paid a lot of money to advertise Brand A! Likewise, if we hear a lot of 'bad news' stories about one particular country we are more liable not to book our holiday in this destination.

The effective leader needs to be able to take a balanced and reflective position despite media influence and develop the skills and tools to be able to help others in the workforce to better analyse and understand how misleading the media might be. Developing critical thinking and helping to develop this in others will prove a useful technique in health and safety leadership.

2.2

ACTIVITY

When making decisions, consider the way in which the representative heuristic might play a role in your thinking. What might the dangers be in health and safety leadership of too much reliance on this method?

Understanding how heuristics affect decisions is critical in developing learning and response in the assessment and management of risk and safety.

Element 2 **Human failure and decision making**

Common perception biases and how they affect decision making

We all may think we can make fair and accurate judgements or evaluations about situations and events, but can we? The way we perceive an event or situation is quite often affected by our own biases. Biases can cause someone to feel or show an inclination or prejudice for or against someone or something. One classic example of perception bias is eyewitness testimony, which is notoriously unreliable because of perception biases that can affect the way people remember and talk about the events they witness.

We need to make many, many rapid decisions all the time, that affect people and situations. We have developed, sometimes unconsciously, methods to do this quickly to arrive at a judgement. Some of these methods have been dealt with earlier. This 'shorthand' can contribute to the formation of perception bias. Other factors, such as social pressure, can contribute to these biases affecting how we perceive situations even when we believe we are being impartial. This includes making assumptions or attributing things that are incorrect, still believing we are right.

> **KEY TERMS**
>
> *Bias*
>
> Inclination or prejudice for or against one person or group, especially in a way considered to be unfair (Oxford Dictionary of English)

We perceive things in very different ways. What do you see?

Young lady or old lady?	Faces or vase?	Jazz player or face?

 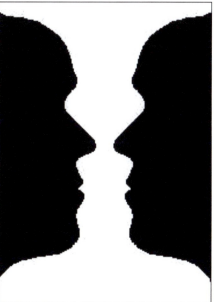 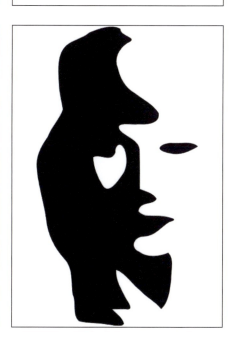

Halo effect

Despite being aware of considerable evidence to the contrary people still seem to use physical attractiveness as a method of assessing personality traits or characteristics; we tend to rate 'attractive' individuals more favourably than those less 'attractive'. This has been referred to as the 'what is beautiful is good' principle, and clearly has absolutely no basis in fact. Yet, the halo effect remains a significant perceptual bias. Put simply it means that if we find one or two attributes of a person 'good' or 'attractive' we tend to be quite happy to assume that everything else about them is the same. One good example of the halo effect in action is our overall impression of celebrities. Since we perceive them as attractive, successful, and often likable, we also tend to see them as intelligent, kind, and funny, although it is proven time and time again this is not always the case.

This is why marketing uses the celebrity 'halo effect' in promoting products or services. When a celebrity is used to endorse a product, the positive feelings felt towards the celebrity can spread to our perceptions of the product itself.

If you are involved in a workplace appraisal of a fellow worker or considering which political candidate to vote for in the next election, consider how the overall impressions may influence your evaluations of other characteristics. Do you really know how good they are in a crisis? Do you really know how well they can do the job? Or is it just that they seem like a 'good' person, and what does that mean anyway?

> *"In the work setting, the halo effect is most likely to show up in a supervisor's appraisal of a subordinate's job performance. In fact, the halo effect is probably the most common bias in performance appraisal. Think about what happens when a supervisor evaluates the performance of a subordinate. The supervisor may give prominence to a single characteristic of the employee, such as enthusiasm, and allow the entire evaluation to be coloured by how he or she judges the employee on that one characteristic. Even though the employee may lack the requisite knowledge or ability to perform the job successfully, if the employee's work shows enthusiasm, the supervisor may very well give him or her a higher performance rating than is justified by knowledge or ability."* [4]

As a leader, people assume that you are all-knowing. It is not enough as a leader to say 'I may not know everything so tell me'; leaders need to take an active role in seeking information.

ACTIVITY

Just because we might be aware of the halo effect does not mean we are immune to it. Like heuristics, bias comes from somewhere other than our rational ability to reason. So how can the effective health and safety leader ensure that decisions are made based on more than a 'feeling'?

Confirmation bias

Confirmation bias occurs when decision makers seek out evidence that confirms their previously held beliefs, while discounting or diminishing the impact of evidence in support of differing conclusions.

Everyone likes to think they are right. When someone believes they know what is right and has confirmation of this, you will often hear statements like "you see, I told you that's how it worked, how could you doubt me?"

Being right is a good sensation. Being wrong however is a totally different feeling and being proven wrong is even worse. This in some way explains why confirmation bias is common. Confirmation bias is based on our desires and pre-existing beliefs; so if you want something to be true you can eventually end up believing this. However, the issue with this is that you will stop gathering evidence about a situation, especially when the evidence that has been collected (that could be very limited) confirms your belief.

We may also refer to people who have a 'selective' memory who choose only to remember, or at least say they remember, only the things they wish to, or that line up with their own beliefs or position.

We are all probably guilty of confirmation bias and may not be aware of it; we all sometimes believe what we want to believe. We will also interpret uncertain evidence to support our existing position.

This is an important bias that good leaders should be aware of. For example, when undertaking investigations, looking at charts and data and in all your conversation, keep a balanced perspective, being open and not narrow minded. Confirmation bias links to being an authentic leader.

Attributing positive results to own personal effort and talent

Self-serving bias

'Well I did work extremely hard and have a natural talent for the subject so I guess that is why I passed so well.'

'I don't know how they expected us to pass, the trainer didn't cover half the topics, also because the blinds were not very good, the sun was in my eyes for half of the exam, so I am not surprised I didn't pass.'

Examine the two statements above. What do you notice about them?

In the first one, which is about success, it is clear that the person attributes their success to personal effort and talent. In the second, which is about failure, it is clearly nothing to do with the individual and the fault lies with other people or conditions. In short this is what self-serving bias is about.

We all need defence mechanisms that will spring into action when we feel we may be under attack. This cognitive bias will help protect our self-esteem. If we attribute positive results to our individual characteristics, we give ourselves a pat on the back and a confidence boost.

By attributing failure to outside conditions or forces, we protect our self-esteem and clear ourselves of personal responsibility. This tendency to attribute blame for negative events to other people should come as no surprise, as few people want to be associated with negativity or be perceived as unsuccessful. People more often seek reassurance about how clever they are and certainly would be unhappy if people thought the opposite. Hence, rather than expose any possible negative traits and accepting that we did not pass the examination because, well, we are not as smart as we thought, we tend to go down the blame route and attempt to find scapegoats for our lack of success. Of course, any positive outcomes, whether down to us or not, we may take credit for in the hope that we will reinforce our positive traits.

The problem with this type of behaviour is that it may protect our self-esteem or confidence (in the short term). However, if we continue to blame external factors for everything, we may not accept the opportunity for self-improvement, choosing instead to blame other people or factors for our misfortune and feeling powerless in addressing our problems. It is also clear that if somebody tries to continually take credit for things they have not done, there will be credibility issues sooner or later.

There is a positive side to self-serving bias to the individual inasmuch as the defence mechanism may help to motivate in the short term. For example, a person believing that the job market is stagnant is preventing them from landing a good job; it may make them more persistent in their job search, at least for a while.

Good leaders will, therefore, look at themselves first if something goes wrong. The leader will want to fully explore the causes of the event; most things that go wrong can be traced back to a management decision.

ACTIVITY

One clear implication of self-serving bias for the health and safety leader is when an incident occurs, people may try to protect themselves by blaming others or other external factors in the work environment.

What are the main negative outcomes from this? How do you think a leader might effectively deal with this challenge?

Hindsight bias

'With the benefit of hindsight, I wouldn't have done it that way.'

'Hindsight bias occurs when people feel that they 'knew it all along', that is, when they believe that an event is more predictable after it becomes known, than it was before it became known.'[5]

A common enough situation; an event takes place, something unusual and random happens to change the outcome of the event, maybe dramatically, and produces a totally different outcome than the one planned or anticipated.

The research carried out by Roese and Vohs says that hindsight bias comes from three inputs:

- cognitive;
- metacognitive; and
- motivational.

The first of these inputs (cognitive) relates to the person selectively recalling information from past incidents; the information recalled is what the person now knows to be true (after the fact). The person will then try to make sense of this but will confuse it with what they thought they knew earlier.

Metacognitive inputs are defined as how easy a past outcome is understood and may be incorrectly applied to its assumed likelihood.

Motivational inputs are a result of people needing to see the world as orderly and predictable and they do not want to be blamed for anything.

When these three inputs combine, the result is that we tend to concentrate on a single point and neglect to take account of other reasonable explanations, therefore, applying hindsight bias.

Hindsight bias has three levels:

- memory distortion (I said it would happen);
- inevitability (it had to happen); and
- foreseeability (I knew it would happen).

Memory distortion relates to a person incorrectly recollecting an early personal judgement.

Inevitability involves personal beliefs about the condition of the world and that past events were predestined. Usually, the inevitable level also includes memory distortion as well as acceptance of beliefs about the factors that cause an event and which make certain outcomes seem more predictable than others.

Foreseeability is very subjective and come from beliefs about the person's own ability and knowledge. It involves the person believing that they could have foreseen an actual event. The foreseeability level also includes the inevitability level; it includes beliefs about the condition of the world as well as including belief about the person's ability to understand the world.

Ultimately, hindsight bias matters because it gets in the way of learning from our experiences. *"If you feel like you knew it all along, it means you won't stop to examine why something really happened,"* observes Roese. *"It's often hard to convince seasoned decision makers that they might fall prey to hindsight bias."* [6]

Good leaders should not jump to conclusions when something goes wrong. A full investigation should be carried out (look at the obscure facts as well as the obvious). This will allow learning from incidents and accidents.

2.2

Habits and decision making

When you think about a habit what comes to mind?

Here is one definition: something that you do often and regularly, sometimes without knowing that you are doing it.

Habits are learned actions that have been reinforced in the past by a reward. They are triggered automatically when we encounter the situation in which we have repeatedly performed those actions before. They are largely outside of our conscious awareness and control. Habits are mentally efficient and allow us to conserve mental resource to use it for more difficult or new tasks.

Habits are likely to persist over time because they are automatic and do not need conscious thought, memory or willpower. Changing a habit takes time and requires conscious self-directed effort and planning.

Habits are something everyone develops over time, good and bad, but how does this influence decision making?

If you think about some of the habits you may have, it will probably become clear quite quickly that these are, again, 'shortcuts' to perform routine tasks without needing to concentrate too deeply on what you are doing. Habits are another way of making us more efficient, by turning routines and often repeated behaviour into a habit, so you do not need to think much about making a coffee or what to have for breakfast or travelling to work. Again the brain turns on autopilot so we can concentrate on more important things.

We do not have to dwell on, ponder or give consideration to every single task in our day, so habits are good.

Well yes, in many ways they are and even if they were not, habits are again part of our subconscious so, as anyone who has tried to discontinue a long-term habit will understand, habits are not easy to break.

Developing 'good' habits can help with the decision-making process. This allows us to focus on the bigger things that need attention and evaluation. It stops us from getting caught up in the day-to-day routine activities that should not require big investments of concentration.

As a leader it is important to recognise that, for most people, your behaviour will be habit and you are, therefore, unaware of doing it. This may include taking risky or unhealthy shortcuts. Your poor habits could influence the workforce eg, not holding the handrail on the stairs, poor DSE behaviour etc.

ACTIVITY

How do you think habits can affect the health and safety decision-making process?

Personal beliefs and how this can affect decision making

Health and safety leaders need to understand how personal beliefs can impact on decision making

Personal belief may or may not line up with that of the majority. Because it is 'personal' it is based on the individual's perspective and formed as a result of the individual's experiences. It is important as belief is connected to, values, attitudes and behaviour, factors which will certainly impact on decision making.

As individuals we all develop personal beliefs over time. We may 'learn' to believe certain things through life experience; we may be taught to believe or may inherit beliefs from our parents or others we respect.

This individualised belief system can exercise a powerful influence over our decision-making processes. Therefore, health and safety leaders need to recognise the types of personal beliefs people have and how they might impact on decisions in the health and safety environment.

Familiarity

It is often more comfortable for people to deal with the familiar than risk the uncertain, or at least it seems that way at the time. Familiarity can often influence us to make assumptions that can be dangerous and misleading. Because a situation may seem 'familiar' as it unfolds, we may ignore the risks and jump to conclusions that we know what will happen next; we probably do not, but our beliefs tell us we do. We also know that humans underestimate risks. Familiarity may also influence a person to stick with what they know rather than look at other alternatives. In an evolving and competitive environment this may not always be useful.

Control acceptance

Organisations put into place controls to help protect the workforce. It is more likely that the workforce will use these controls if they believe that they will work. As a health and safety leader it is crucial to ensure that you know what these controls are and use them if relevant. This is going to have a positive impact on the workforce. It is also essential that you ensure that all workers know what controls are in place, why they are there and, most importantly, that they know how to use the controls safely and effectively.

Self-efficacy

This put simply, is about self-belief, a powerful factor in many decision-making processes. In order to overcome obstacles or challenges and achieve a desired outcome a person needs to believe in themselves, to have confidence in their ability to set and achieve objectives. Yes, this may at some stage be based on measuring previous experience, but initially at least, as an athlete must believe in their ability to break a record, a leader must believe themselves capable of delivering on a target. It is a very strong and positive personal belief, but the opposite may also be true with low self-esteem preventing people from even attempting to succeed in a task. It is important for a health and safety leader to recognise self-efficacy as a factor in the way people perform and to build the capabilities of the team.

Responsibility

Responsibility and integrity are key 'personal beliefs' in many endeavours. In effective health and safety leadership more so; a clearly defined understanding that everyone has responsibility for health and safety will be an essential component in developing a successful health and safety culture. As a health and safety leader you should ensure that your teams believe they have the responsibility for health and safety. To do this you should be ensuring that they can take ownership of situations and make non-critical health and safety decisions for themselves. You also empower them to challenge others who are acting in an unsafe manner.

Normative beliefs

'What would they expect me to do?' and 'How would my team expect me to behave in this situation?' are examples of how normative beliefs work. It is based on the prevailing culture and how we think, others (probably others we care about or respect) would expect us to behave. This is important in a decisional-making process simply because most people would sooner have the 'approval' of others about a decision than not. We all seek approval of one sort or another and anticipating that our actions would meet with approval will have a bearing on the decision we make.

Consequences

Understanding the consequences of our actions will clearly have an impact on and influence our decisions. Whether this is a simple uncomplicated choice or a much more complex process, evaluating what the consequences of this decision will be will assist in determining the choice that is made. When considering the consequences we generally tend to reflect on when they will occur as well as what they are. There are occasions where unsafe behaviours will not have a consequence for some time, but others where it will happen immediately. For example an individual may believe that exposure to dust from not wearing RPE may possibly lead to an occupational illness in many years, whereas not wearing RPE will definitely have the immediate consequence of getting the job done quicker. The consequences that we believe to be soon and certain are the ones that exert the most influence on our behaviour. We can tend to think 'it won't happen to me' or that 'it won't happen immediately so I can leave someone else to sort it out'.

A health and safety leader should, therefore, ensure that reward/recognition/praise is given at all times for the presence of safe and healthy behaviour. This will help to ensure that your organisation will be seen as a caring employer. On the flip side of this, if workers know that you will walk past and ignore unsafe behaviours this is reinforcing unsafe behaviours and can negatively impact on the safety culture.

Element 2 references / further reading

References

1 Reducing error and influencing behaviour, HSG48, HSE Books, ISBN: 978-0-7176-2452-2
http://www.hse.gov.uk/pUbns/priced/hsg48.pdf

2 Improving compliance with safety procedures, Reducing industrial violations, HSE Books, ISBN: 978-0-7176-0970-7
http://www.hse.gov.uk/humanfactors/topics/improvecompliance.pdf

3 Applied Social Psychology, 2012 - Schneider FW, Gruman J A and Coutts L M

4 and 5 Hindsight Bias, Neal Roese and Kathleen D. Voha
https://carlsonschool.umn.edu/sites/carlsonschool.umn.edu/files/faculty/publications/roese_vohs_hindsight_bias_2012_pps_0.pdf

Further reading

Because we are only human
https://www.healthandsafetyatwork.com/behavioural-safety/nebosh-only-human

To err is human: human error and workplace safety, Safety and Health Practitioner article
https://www.shponline.co.uk/to-err-is-human-human-error-and-workplace-safety/

Notes

Leadership

This chapter will explore the different types of leadership styles. It will then go on to examine the HSE's health and safety leadership model's five leadership values and supporting foundations. You will find that the five leadership values are the basis for the qualification assessment. Finally, the chapter will look at how effective leadership communication can help to build relationships and rapport with the workforce.

The HSE's model is based upon an amalgamation of different types of leadership styles. The HSE model is an evidence based model that draws upon HSE's research (including HSE Research Report 952) which identified the key characteristics of good health and safety leadership.

Learning outcomes

- The meaning of transformational, authentic, resonant and transactional leadership styles
- The application of the five values and supporting foundations of the HSE's health and safety leadership model
- How relationships with the workforce can be built by effective leadership communication.

Different leadership styles

This section will examine a number of different approaches or theories of leadership and how they might be used by the effective health and safety leader.

There are many differing styles of leader and many theories of leadership, far too many to look at in detail at this stage. However, it is important for any aspiring health and safety leader to appreciate at least a small selection of leadership styles, what they comprise of and how they may be used to influence different groups of people.

When evaluating the impact of a leader, people sometimes wrongly believe that they have only one style. While this is possible, it is unlikely for an effective leader. One of the key skills in leadership is recognising how people are motivated in a variety of situations and adapting the leadership technique to fit the situation. It would be challenging and ultimately problematic for a health and safety leader to adopt a 'one size fits all approach'. By examining these four approaches we will be able to compare and contrast each method and how each one encourages people to follow.

The transformational leader

The transformational leader focuses unsurprisingly on 'transforming' people within an organisation to help and support each other as well as the organisation as a whole. For this to take place the transformational leader must build respect and loyalty in those who follow. By creating a culture based on admiration and trust, this theory suggests that people will be willing to work harder, support one another and give more to the organisation than would otherwise be the case.

Followers trusting and following their leader

In short, the transformational leader will generate trust, respect and admiration from followers which are considered important facilitators to motivate people to perform beyond expectations. They can have a positive impact on safety by leading by example and acting as safety role models; they will demonstrate a high priority for safety over other organisational goals. In addition, they encourage workers to work toward higher standards of safety and to try out new ways of working safely. They demonstrate a real concern for the well-being and safety of workers and will demonstrate respect for the views and opinions of others. They have a positive influence on safety by enhancing perceived fairness and worker organisational commitment and creating a positive safety culture. The transformational leader will be a supportive presence and is unlikely to be egotistical or self-important as both these attributes will have a negative impact on transformational leadership.[1]

Here are some of the characteristics of transformational leaders:

- organised and inspire creativeness from followers/colleagues;
- works well with teams, workers will identify with them and they encourage followers to work together to achieve the best results;
- respectful to others and therefore respected by others;
- they will articulate a vision that followers can aspire to and seek to attain;
- they challenge assumptions and traditional ways of doing things, invite new ideas and encourage followers to 'think outside of the box';
- create a supportive climate and promote learning opportunities to meet the followers' needs;
- takes responsibility for actions as well as encouraging others to take responsibility; and
- creates a culture of respect based on rapport and positive relationships.

ACTIVITY

Why do you think this style of leadership may be useful for the health and safety leader? Can you think of any negative aspects to this method?

3.1

Conventional leadership

Transactional leadership

Transactional leadership will, for many people, probably appear familiar and possibly what 'conventional' leadership has looked like in many organisations. The transactional leader is all about the 'status quo' and the tools here will include:

- **contingent reward** - leaders agree with followers' specific goals with commensurate rewards for effort and commitment;

- **active management** - leaders actively monitor the workforce to ensure their behaviours, routines and processes comply with expected standards and intervene before problems arise (leaders check that the rules are being followed); and

- **passive management** - the leader will usually only intervene after a problem has occurred.

The transactional leader is more likely to be found in established organisations, where the workforce is used to patterns and tried-and-tested methods of improving productivity. The motivation here is almost entirely to do with self-interest or fear of consequences of under-performance or non-compliance.

Transactional and transformational leadership theories are often compared, and the following table will show you the main differences.

Transactional	v	Transformational
Leadership is responsive.		A proactive leadership process built on rapport.
Works well within the organisational culture and hierarchical structure.		New ideas from various sources are implemented to bring about change to the organisational culture.
Workers accomplish objectives through either rewards or penalties set by the leader.		Appeals to the workforce's moral values or higher ideals to achieve organisational and individual objectives.
Motivation is based on rewards designed to appeal to worker's self-interest.		Motivation is based on the interest of the group or the 'bigger picture' rather than individual self-interest.

ACTIVITY

Much of the writing around motivation theory and leadership styles places more emphasis on the value of transformational or authentic styles. This suggests that real motivation factors are more to do with self-development than material wins.

Do you think this is valid?

Does the transactional method have value, if so in what circumstances do you think it is most appropriate?

How might you adopt this style as part of your health and safety leadership communications mix?

Authentic leadership

Authentic leadership is a relatively new leadership style built on extremely old theory or principals; these pre-date many of the more conventional theories by many centuries. The roots of authentic leadership are based on ancient Greek philosophy 'know thyself'. Authentic leaders are defined as those who are self-aware, confident, genuine, optimistic, moral/ethical, balanced in terms of decision making, and transparent in enacting leadership. Recent research shows links between authentic leadership and positive safety climate (Nielsen et al., 2013; Borgensen et al., 2013 study in the shipping industry in Journal of Leadership and Organisational Studies).

There are obvious similarities between authentic leadership and transformational leadership. Certainly, the key attributes of the authentic leader would be a great advantage in transformational leadership, these include:

- Self-awareness ('know thyself'). A prerequisite for being an authentic leader. This is about understanding your own strengths and weaknesses as well as recognising your values. Authentic leadership requires that you really know what you stand for, alongside honestly recognising that you value is critical. Becoming self-aware is the first step in developing the other components that make up authentic leadership.

- Relational transparency or 'being genuine'. This is about being genuine and honest in your relationships with others. A straightforward approach with no concealed agendas or power games. The authentic leader will ensure that people will know where they stand whether they like it or not. Honesty sometimes means making tough decisions.

- Balanced processing or 'fair-mindedness'. This means listening to others, including opposing viewpoints that are actively sought by an effective authentic leader. Planning is a key characteristic with discussion of options available before choosing a direction. This is no solitary enterprise and everyone's views are important.

- Internalised moral perspective or 'doing the right thing'. Ethics and fairness are driving forces of the authentic leader with no room for personal gain at other people's expense, dishonesty or exploitation. Leadership here will have goals that are not self-serving and will depend on the authentic leader's moral compass to ensure the 'right' outcome for all concerned.

As you will appreciate, the authentic leader will set ambitious standards for themselves as well as everyone else. Success will be a team effort and based on the principal of win-win, not always easy to achieve in many organisations. However, this style of leadership has gained ground during the past 30 years in many areas; clearly following an authentic leader can be a rewarding and satisfying experience.

It is challenging to attempt to be an authentic leader, it takes strength of character to recognise your own shortcomings. You need to really reflect and get to know yourself and develop the courage and strength to do the 'right' thing. In truth there are many leaders who are far from authentic, and clearly corruption and lack of morality are all too common, hence the search for 'good' people to lead is becoming compelling.

ACTIVITY

How do you feel about the idea of authentic leadership in health and safety?

How important do you think it is that a leader demonstrates their intention to do the 'right' thing?

What other benefits might this bring to an organisation as well as individuals?

Resonant leadership

Emotional intelligence (EI or EQ)

During the past 20 years or so there have been some very substantial changes in leadership and management styles as well as organisational and cultural behaviour. This has included a significant and growing awareness of the usefulness of unconventional tools and techniques in business and the world of work. Resonant leadership has three dimensions:

- mindfulness;
- hope; and
- compassion.

Mindfulness – leading a life by developing a complete and conscious awareness of self, others, environment and work; being awake and being aware.

Hope – enables us to believe that our goals are achievable; this motivates us to inspire others to reach those goals while striving to achieve them ourselves. They may dream about a better future and believe they can attain this and will, therefore, develop an optimistic point of view.

Compassion – helps us to include emotions when thinking, making decisions and taking action. The resonant leader will empathise with others and will try to put themselves in another's position; this will treat superiors and subordinates equally with empathy and compassion.

Resonant leaders will be in tune with those around them and the leadership style is based on the emotional intelligence concept and has been championed by amongst others, the U.S. scientist and psychologist Daniel Goleman.

It is defined on the Institute for Health and Human Potential Website[2]. Emotional intelligence (EQ or EI) is a term created by two researchers – Peter Salavoy and John Mayer – and popularized by Dan Goleman in his 1996 book of the same name. We define EI as the ability to recognise, understand and manage our own emotions. Recognise, understand and influence the emotions of others.

In practical terms, this means being aware that emotions can drive our behaviour and impact people (positively and negatively) and learning how to manage those emotions – both our own and others – especially when we are under pressure.

You will see obvious parallels with some of the concepts discussed earlier in the sections on transformational and authentic leadership as emotional intelligence requires that a leader understands and has control over their own feelings and drives to effectively understand how to best have an impact on the behaviour of those around them.

Emotional intelligence is also a key ingredient in resonant leadership which Goleman suggests comprises four styles.

Visionary

Visionary leaders, know where they want go, share that vision and take people with them by inspiring them to want to follow. While the visionary leader will lead from the front, they will expect those who follow to think for themselves and understand the part they are playing in the 'bigger picture'. This will build resonance by making people feel part of something and motivating them to achieve a shared goal. This style of leadership is suitable when organisational changes are taking place or when a clear direction needs to be communicated and implemented effectively.

Coaching

Coaching is a valuable tool that focuses on the individual personal development of those in a team. Using a coaching style of leadership will demonstrate genuine interest in the workforce and thus enable leaders to build trust and rapport. Coaching has been proven to motivate people to achieve more, building resonance by linking people's needs with organisation's goals. Coaching is highly effective in improving worker performance and conveying a sense of value to the individual.

Affiliative

Based on the previously discussed emotional intelligence an affiliative leader will strive to build collaborative relationships using empathy. The key here is to demonstrate that the leader really values others and cares about their feelings. By linking people together, the affiliative leader builds resonance by creating harmonious relationships that promotes interdependence. This style of leadership can help with bringing together or strengthening a team and building performance over time.

Democratic

A democratic leader will appreciate the importance of understanding the feelings and valuing the opinions within a diverse group. They will use the expertise and knowledge that exists within the group through collaboration and teamwork, to achieve shared goals. The democratic leader will need to be a highly effective communicator with particularly good listening skills. Empathy is a key attribute for the democratic leader.

By valuing people's input and attaining commitment the democratic leader can build resonance. They can obtain buy-in from team members for projects or change that must be led within an organisation.

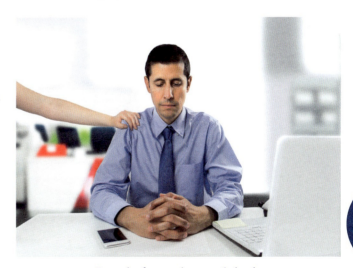

Empathy from a democratic leader

ACTIVITY

What do you think are the key benefits for adopting a resonant or transactional leadership style in health and safety?

Can you think of any examples of where this style of leadership may be essential to getting the job done?

Can you also think about why it may need to be carefully managed?

CASE STUDY

A construction company decided that they needed to get the workforce more involved in decision making.

"In the past, the management of the organisation was resistant to the idea of worker involvement in policy making and suspicious of any perceived dilution of its authority."

The company changed its Board and due to this the opportunity was taken to involve the workforce more in consultation.

"The new Board of Directors understood what we wanted to do and were happy to support the idea of worker engagement/consultation. This meant that we had a 'blank canvas' on which to place whatever engagement/consultation mechanism we felt was most appropriate, so obviously it was important to get this right."

The company formed a Consultation Committee which, other than the Health and Safety Director, is formed entirely from the workforce. The company has benefited from this change; workers are owning health and safety and have seen improved relationships throughout the organisation.

3.2 The supporting foundations of the leadership values

You will have already seen a few of the leadership values in some of the earlier chapters of this book. The remaining values will be looked at in more detail later in this section. However, to recap, the five leadership values are:

- building and promoting a shared health and safety vision;
- being considerate and responsive;
- providing support and recognition;
- promoting fairness and trust in relationships with others; and
- encouraging improvement, innovation and learning.

Underpinning these values there are also three foundations of leadership that we will now look at in more detail. The underpinning values are:

- involvement and communication;
- effective role modelling; and
- embedding robust health and safety management as a business norm.

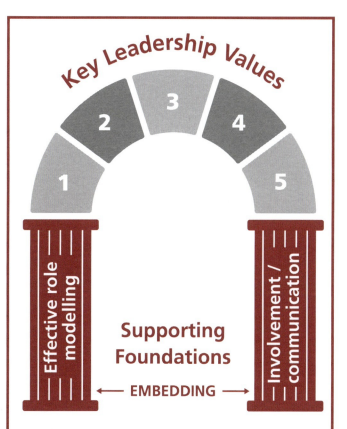

ACTIVITY

Think about your own role within your own organisation in relation to the leadership values and foundations.

Do you think that all of these principles are applied?

Can you provide some examples of this? If not, what might be the reasons for this?

The health and safety leader must be proactive right across the organisation. The leader must ensure that their organisation is not just paying 'lip service' to the subject but that health and safety is incorporated into the business. The health and safety leader should be passionate and vocal about health and safety so ensure that it stays at the core of the business. The leadership values will ensure that every part of the workforce can play a part in the delivery of the highest standards of health and safety.

Later we will examine the importance of adapting the leadership style; we will also look at the mix of communication methods and media needed to ensure strong positive relationships and rapport are built across the organisation.

We will now look at each of the foundations in turn.

Involvement and communication

Effective two-way conversations are a useful tool for the health and safety leader

As a health and safety leader, you should be proactive in creating and using opportunities to have two-way conversations with all workers relating to health and safety issues. You must ensure that you are consistent in your health and safety messages; the message should be targeted and tailored to the audience across the organisation. It is also vitally important that you make sure that the messages contained within any communications have been received and understood. We will look at this in more detail shortly when we look at building a rapport with the workforce and communication.

As well as the above you should be involving the workforce in all aspects of health and safety where and when relevant and appropriate to do so. Empowering the workforce to make decisions is a very powerful tool. Not only will this make individual workers look at their own health and safety behaviours it will also make them look at their colleagues' behaviours as well. This will give your workers the confidence to challenge those who are acting in an unsafe manner.

Effective role modelling

Leading by example makes the workforce want to follow you

As a health and safety leader your behaviour will be witnessed and judged by the rest of the workforce; it is, therefore, very important that you lead by example eg, by wearing the correct personal protective equipment where appropriate and relevant. It is very unlikely that the workforce will follow safety rules if they see that you are breaking them consistently, or if you ignore others who are carrying out unsafe actions. You should take every opportunity to demonstrate your personal commitment; the more you do, the more it will be noticed. Having leaders visibly demonstrate safe behaviours show the workforce that it is not 'one rule for them' and one rule for the organisation's management.

Embedding

Embedding is about ensuring that health and safety is not considered as a stand-alone activity. It is imperative that health and safety is embedded into the organisation at all levels and that it is considered critical for business success. Health and safety should be seen as just one tool to help support your organisation's purpose.

Being considerate and responsive (health and safety leadership value 2)

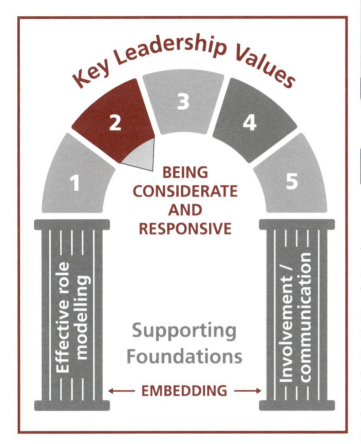

People generally respond to people who demonstrate empathy towards them. As we have already discussed, certain leadership styles and theories are built on developing skills of empathy and emotional intelligence.

Considering other people's ideas and points of view

There are many methods of demonstrating responsiveness and consideration and we look at some of these elsewhere. What we should be trying to achieve here is treating people how you want to be treated yourself. Listening and responding appropriately is a skill a good leader should possess. This of course, does not mean that you as a leader can agree with everything everyone says, but it does mean you should listen and demonstrate that you are interested in everyone's views or concerns. Equally, responding to other people's needs will continue the good work of building effective relationships. If a training need is identified, within reason this need should be met. If there is a gap in the knowledge or skill set of people in the workforce that prevents them from undertaking the tasks required of them as part of the health and safety vision, training or coaching should be made available where and when possible. This is about investing in the people you need to make the vision happen.

ASSESSMENT ACTIVITY 4

Please refer to the document Unit HSL1, guidance and information for candidates and internal assessors.

You should now complete task
L2: Being considerate and responsive.

Assessing own health and safety leadership performance

One of the most important things that a health and safety leader should do is to critically evaluate themselves. Our perception of ourselves may be very different to the perceptions of others in the workforce. You will usually have some form of upwards performance evaluation (personal development review or similar) but there are usually no formal processes to receive evaluation from the rest of the workforce.

To improve your leadership style there are two important things you should be doing. Firstly, you should question the workforce. You do not have to do this every week but maybe every six months or so. It is important that the workforce know that there will be no recriminations from their responses. You should ask the workforce the right questions; open questions usually produce a better response than a closed question. So, for example, don't ask the workforce "am I a good leader?"; inevitably the response here is going to be 'yes' which is helping no-one. A much better question would be "What one thing do you think I could do to make me a better leader?" However, it is not just about asking the questions it is also about listening to the response and taking on-board and dealing with any criticism.

The other thing you should be practicing is self-reflection. You should also try to carry out this activity out every six months. The process involves considering any actions you have taken during that time and analysing them to find out whether you could have done anything better or differently. Very often, carrying out some form of continual professional development will help with this exercise.

As a leader you should be striving to always improve your performance and how others see you. Undertaking these activities will help you to achieve this goal.

"Who would like to give me feedback on my leadership qualities?"

Building relationships with the workforce

This section deals with the part played by building relationships or rapport with the workforce using a variety of communication techniques and strategies.

Creating and sustaining a positive relationship with the workforce is a key consideration for most organisations. An effective health and safety leader will understand that maintaining a dialogue with the workforce provides the right environment for sharing and promoting the health and safety vision, as well as ensuring that effective communication is taking place.

Here we examine ways in which effective relationships can be formed and maintained using a variety of tried and tested leadership techniques and strategies.

Leadership walkabouts and rapport

One very successful strategy that may be employed is managing by walking about (MBWA) (or wandering around); MBWA is an accepted management technique. This has not always been the case; many organisations have strict hierarchical structures and much more of a 'closed door' policy than is normal today.

Building rapport is an important skill for the health and safety leader

The idea of managers walking around in the working environment engaging with the workforce is now considered the norm. This creates an environment where workers feel comfortable raising concerns. Maintaining this style of organisational culture, encouraging managers to engage directly, frequently and informally, with front line workers, asking for their views and opinions for improvements, as well as identifying any issues or problems, is very well suited to the MBWA technique.

Walkabouts should not be treated as a tick box exercise to meet management KPI's. They need to involve two way communication - think about the purpose and value of the walkabout from the workers' point of view also.

It also provides an excellent learning opportunity for managers to observe workforce activity first hand and work directly with front line workers to resolve problems.

The benefits of using this technique to establish rapport with people from right across an organisation should be self-evident, after all it is widely accepted that face-to-face communication is often the most effective way of delivering and ensuring information has been received and understood. So, what actually is 'rapport' and why is it important in health and safety leadership?

> **KEY TERM**
>
> *Rapport*
>
> *A close and harmonious relationship in which the people or groups concerned understand each other's feelings or ideas and communicate well.*
> (Oxford English Dictionary)

By establishing rapport with colleagues and the workforce, the effective health and safety leader is able to understand other people's feelings and communicate well; both vital factors for the successful management of health and safety.

It is important to remember that while MBWA should be frequent and largely informal, focus is also important. It is also worth remembering that the most effective communication is usually planned so we will take a look at some methods to assist with that later in this section.

In broad terms, though planning for leadership walkabouts can be divided into four sections.

MBWA frequency

To be effective and build positive relationships there is no point in just walking about randomly talking to a few people once and expecting to achieve anything. Building rapport will require a number of key factors; reliability, trust, active listening and continuity. These things can only be achieved through regular positive encounters with the workforce. Clearly, the timings of these conversations will largely depend upon organisational/personal needs and certainly should not become a barrier or unwelcome interruption to the flow of work. However, if people are to be encouraged to interact and share thoughts, feelings and reactions some kind of pattern would be a good strategy. Perhaps there is a specific time during the working week where workgroups/teams may be more responsive/not so busy?

MBWA format

Once timings and frequency have been established the next consideration will probably be around 'how' this activity will take place. Again, this will greatly depend on the circumstances/environment/industry that provides the setting. Establishing a format that people can identify with and can be used to best effect will be essential if you are to establish a good rapport and make the MBWA activity worthwhile. For example, you could use the 'Safe Deal'[3] cards that have been produced by the Health and Safety Laboratory. The cards contain questions that you could ask your workforce to open dialogue which could be either formal or informal. Alternatively, you could devise your own list of questions to use as a prompt when you are walking around, or you may wish to use a tick list. Some questions you may want to consider are:

- Open questions (TEDS: Tell, Explain, Describe, Show).
- 'Are we looking after your health and safety?'
- 'What would make being healthy and safe easier?'
- 'What would you like to change about health and safety here?'
- Ask in the third person: 'why would someone do that job like that?'
- 'What's slow, inconvenient or uncomfortable about doing this safely?'
- What is it they are telling themselves 'It will never happen to me' and ask them 'What if it did happen?'

It is worth bearing in mind that the walkabout should ultimately produce tangible outputs. It is a process that will involve giving and receiving information, acting on this information, reflecting on what happens and understanding what should happen next; a continuous process.

One, sure-fire way of ruining any kind of rapport or positive relationship is by asking people questions, getting their answers and then doing absolutely nothing with them or not providing any kind of feedback. It is also a significant waste of time and resources. So, devising a format for your MBWA is an essential step.

ACTIVITY

What does leadership walkabout mean to you?

How do you apply it/what format do you use?

What more could you do?

When do you do your walkabouts?

Lessons learned

As discussed above, a key part of this activity revolves around gathering information, or 'intelligence' if you prefer. An effective health and safety leader needs to better understand the attitudes or behaviours of the workforce to a process, or learn more about how particular activities are prioritised. If they are looking for effective ways of encouraging people to participate in the decision-making process, records of encounters that took place during an MBWA activity need to be clear and accurate. This will allow all those involved to learn from the process and feed this information back into the cycle. Lessons learned will be of significant value in making future decisions or planning how to introduce new health and safety initiatives. The reflective process will add value to the technique and, used in conjunction with frequency and format, will provide valuable lessons and modifications for future practice.

Taking action

One valuable method of taking action is to analyse a process, product or service is SWOT. A simple model that looks at Strengths, Weaknesses, Opportunities and Threats.

However, the drawback of this is that it may just become a paper exercise. If there are no tangible outputs from the process there is no point in wasting your time in carrying it out. If there are no outputs that the workforce can see, they are less likely to engage with you in the future.

The same is also true about any ideas for improvement received from the workforce. Even if the idea/suggestion has been considered previously. It is always important to feedback to the workforce; you need to let them know whether the idea will be taken forward or, if not, why not.

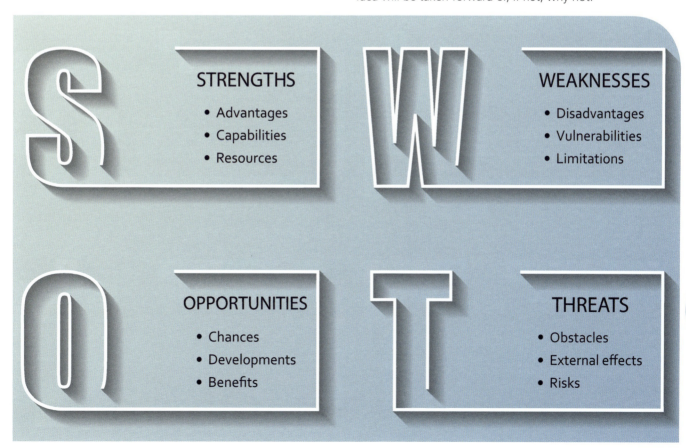

ACTIVITY

How might you use the SWOT tool to analyse the MBWA method?

What might the strengths be of such a process?

Where might it fall short (weaknesses)?

What type of opportunities could be revealed?

Which areas might produce a threat?

Effective communication in building rapport

Rapport is primarily about building trust and respect to promote good two way communication. In addition to messages delivered by leaders, it will also help to ensure that messages delivered by the workforce are received, understood and acted upon.

Building rapport will help ensure that the messages delivered by the health and safety leader are:

- received;
- understood; and
- acted on.

Clearly this requires that effective communication takes place, obvious really? But, what is effective communication and how do we ensure we are doing it right? Sometimes it is easy to think that because you have said something, asked for something, conveyed some valuable information, that everyone has got the message. Wrong! Communication does not work that way, were that the case everyone would be first class communicators and every process would run smoothly, is this the case for you?

What sort of factors did you have? When we talk of noise it can mean actual noise but also the everyday factors that prevent messages being received the way they should, that clog up the communication process and lead to misunderstandings and problems, have a negative effect on relationship building and most certainly provide no help whatsoever in building a good rapport. Did your list included things like: time (as in timely delivery as well as lack of time), place (environment), physical noise, language (both spoken and body), attitude, stereotyping, prejudice, stress, culture, pressure of work? You will appreciate that effective communication is far from being 'simple'.

ACTIVITY

Make a list of some of the barriers to effective communication (either face-to-face or other means such as email) you can think of. These might be physical and may include things like attitude, environment, culture, stereotyping.

Barriers to building a good rapport with the workforce

Communication is an art and a science that requires understanding and practice to get it right. Some people may be born communicators, but most of us need to learn how to communicate effectively as we would learn to speak another language or any other skill.

There are always barriers to communication. Let us have a look at some of the hurdles you face on a daily basis. The fact is, you cannot eliminate all these barriers. What you can do is:

- identify those in your working environment;
- take account of them, and adapt your message and its delivery; and
- reduce their negative influence on your communication.

Many 'audiences' are not really audiences. Quite often, they are not ready or not waiting for your message. Some audiences may be ready for you but too busy. However, they may also be irritated, distracted or simply uninterested. A good leader will recognise this and plan for it.

Health and safety leaders need to plan communications to reach the whole audience; your message could lose impact if just one person does not engage/starts to look bored.

You also have different audiences to consider. Within those separate groups, there will always be a range of attitudes, beliefs and behaviours. If you bear this in mind when communicating, it might help you to interpret or understand the responses you get. Try and remember this during meetings, consultations and encounters with the workforce.

Health and safety leaders need to plan communications to reach the whole audience; your message could lose impact if just one person does not engage/starts to look bored.

The attitude and behaviour of those with whom you need to communicate can also affect the impact of your communication. This could include:

- a history of negative attitudes or a culture of mistrust; and
- previous management failure to build rapport or trust with the workforce.

What about the physical environment that you communicate in? Is there anything that could realistically be changed? Sometimes it is worth thinking twice before starting a conversation if the environment does not work.

Consider:

- distractions, interruptions and noise;
- lack of resources;
- occupational stress; and
- workspace, layout, comfort.

When using the MBWA technique you will need to be mindful of these issues.

What good communication looks like

In planning communication and conveying information there are a few things worth considering, a useful guide is the seven C's of effective communication. This will help you ensure that the right information is given.

Clear   State what you mean so people can understand.

Concise   Leave no uncertainty, provide facts.

Concrete Solid, dependable and real.

Correct   Is it right in presentation, delivery, style, and time?

Coherent Does it make sense, really make sense?

Complete Nothing missing, no chance of misunderstanding?

Courteous Friendly, open and honest, no hidden agenda?

Applying these rules can help ensure that information is 'right' and suitable for purpose, therefore, avoiding misinformation or difficulty interpreting what is needed.

Physiology, voice, words

In addition to the above you should consider each of the following which are ranked in importance of use.

Physiology

When face-to-face with an audience it is important that you try to match and mirror your audiences':

- posture;
- gestures;
- facial expressions;
- eye contact; and
- breathing.

Voice

You should try to ensure that you match and mirror your audiences':

- tone of voice;
- pitch;
- frequency;
- speed;
- timbre;
- characteristics;
- quality; and
- volume.

With physiology and voice it is important that you try to do this to put people at ease. However, you must try not to be too obvious about this as your audience may think that you are deliberately imitating them to make fun of them and they could become immediately hostile. Leaders should ultimately be trying to persuade the audience to take part in effective communication.

Words

For each audience consider:

- consider the content and what words you will use (ie do not use street slang when addressing a board of directors);
- avoid using jargon unless you are sure that your audience knows and understands what you are talking about; and
- try to include any shared experiences or interests to put your audience at ease.

We sometimes forget the most important part of communication, the receiver or audience. If they have not let us know they have received and understood the message, communication has not taken place. This is where the importance of rapport becomes even clearer. In order for a piece of communication to take place it requires a loop:

sender, sends a message, via a communication channel;

receiver, receives the message, understands it;

receiver, sends feedback to sender; and

sender, confirms the receiver's understanding of the message.

This can be as simple as:

Sender: 'I will meet you in the coffee shop at 10.00'

Receiver: 'What, the one on the high street next to the station at 10.00 this morning?'

Sender: 'Yes'

This is a complete communication loop. The same feedback rule would apply to a complex email or detailed conversation. Unless there has been confirmation of understanding and a signal of action, communication has not taken place.

In face-to-face communication we have the advantage of occupying the same physical space at the same time, hence MBWA eliminates many of the barriers to communication. It is easier to gauge whether your information has been received correctly when your audience is in front of you. It is essential to get the 'receiver' to confirm the message, especially where safety critical information is involved. This method can also be used during non-face-to-face verbal delivery (telephone call, video conferencing etc). You may want to ask for a written response from any written communications especially those that are sent by email, text message or similar.

The right information, praise and questions

The point of any communication is to provide accurate information to another party (audience). It is, therefore, essential that you provide your audience with the right information the first time you send it. Your workforce is unlikely to have confidence in your leadership if, for example, you have to keep sending emails to correct previous emails that contained incorrect information.

Another part of communication is using it to praise people. If you see someone doing something to improve safety or challenging someone else's behaviour, praise them. It does not matter when you do this or what communication method you use, as long as it is done (receiving praise makes us feel better). In other cases you should be asking questions and generally showing an interest in the way the workforce are working. The more you ask, the more the workforce will remember you. This could have a positive impact going forward as workers will see you as someone who is open to communication and someone who will take account of their views.

3.3

ACTIVITY

Information overload:
do you sometimes feel overwhelmed by the amount of information you are expected to process?

How much of it is of real value?

How do you prioritise what you need?

How do you know what you need, without examining everything?

"There are known knowns. These are things we know that we know. There are known unknowns. That is to say, there are things that we know we don't know. But there are also unknown unknowns. There are things we don't know we don't know."
(Donald Rumsfeld 2002)

Time is an enemy in many aspects of our lives. When you want to tell someone something important, consider the timing of the message and ask yourself the following questions:

- How is time going to affect the medium you choose?
- Is this the only or best time to communicate?
- Can you put all other concerns aside for a minute?
- Can you help your audience to do the same?
- Is everybody clear about how long this will take?

Of course, it is not practical to expect to have the perfect time and place for the delivery of important information or to engage in conversations with the workforce, life does not work that way. But it is worth considering the ways in which barriers can at least be minimised to obtain the best result you can. The successful health and safety leader will plan to mitigate as many negative effects as possible to ensure the maximum impact of information given.

Element 3 **Leadership**

VROOM'S MODEL OF MOTIVATION

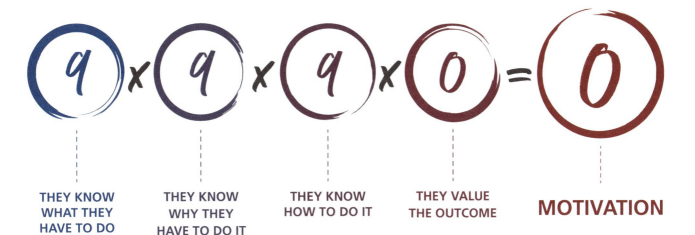

Vroom's Model of Motivation

An understanding of some of the ways in which people are motivated may assist in designing or planning appropriate methods used to communicate effectively and build relationships.

Amongst motivation theories is Victor Vroom's expectancy theory of motivation. This is a tried and tested model used extensively to demonstrate how people's attitudes can be determined on the basis of several crucial factors. It is worth exploring how this works and how it can help the health and safety leader to structure the information, plan an appropriate method of delivery and be ready to counter any resistance that may emerge.

Vroom proposed that a worker's performance is based on a number of factors that include: skills, ability, personality, knowledge and experience. He suggested that while each individual will have different goals, people can be motivated providing they believe that they:

- know what they are required to do;
- know why they have to do it;
- have the skills to do it effectively (they know how to do it); and
- value the outcome.

Vroom's model is an equation. Each part of the equation is given a score out of 10; if any part of the equation is 0 then the level of motivation will be 0.

The theory is based upon the following factors:

Valence: Is this reward (promotion/training/job change/process) I keep hearing about, something I want? (Do I want it?).

Instrumentality: If I perform as anticipated, will it actually happen? (Can I get it?).

Expectancy: If I do as requested and assist with bringing about the change(s), will I be able to perform the tasks well and not struggle? (Will I do well with it?).

Vroom's theory is useful for an effective leader as it demonstrates why the workforce and individual workers behave the way they do. It focuses on their perceptions of your actions. Are you unknowingly attempting to reward them with something they do not want? Is there doubt about fairness? Is there insecurity about how they will do well with the reward you are trying to give them?

Leading will be considerably easier when the members of the workforce want to do what you expect of them. This is where rapport, communication and relationship building combine to provide powerful results.

Element 3 Leadership

How information can be given

We have discussed some of the methods that the health and safety leader may use to communicate and build relationships with the workforce. We can now focus on some of the crucial factors that can have an impact on how this information is received. It is important that we remember that communication has only taken place when the message has been received and understood and that we have some kind of feedback that this has happened.

Here we will examine what should be taken into account when we give information to others as well as how to effectively gather useful information.

Primacy/recency effect

If you consider the way you personally absorb information, it will provide you with some good ideas about how other people may respond to your own efforts to communicate information. Most people share characteristics in the way we learn and take things in. Take for example a short course, maybe a bit like this one. At the start, most people will be alert and ready to receive the information, in the right state of mind, prepared and hopefully, interested. So, there will be focus on the information at the beginning and this will normally mean it will be remembered. This is the primacy effect. At the end of the course there will be summarising and discussion, again because this is fresh in the mind, people will generally pay attention here and the information will stick, this is called the recency effect.

What this means is the process of giving information is reflected in many processes, from learning theory to advertising. Make sure you state the important things at the start of the communication process (primacy) and at the end, recap the important points (recency). This should ensure that the essential information is received and committed to memory or acted upon.

Language and jargon

We looked at some barriers to communication earlier, but it is worth looking in more detail at the part played by language and jargon in giving information. When we talk about language in communication terms this is not necessarily about how difficult it would be to convey meaningful information; such as in English to an exclusively Arabic-speaking workforce, although this would, of course, be challenging. Language is also to do with dialect, perception, physical or body language, levels of understanding and the use of jargon. To give information effectively it is essential to 'know your audience'; who are they? What do they do? What do they know? How do they feel? How will they feel about the information you are about to communicate? Knowing your audience will help you to use the 'right' language. It will allow you to judge how technical your message should be, to assess the correct tone for this particular group and very importantly, how much jargon you should use, if at all?

Jargon is either a useful shortcut for people with a shared understanding or knowledge of a subject, or a baffling and extremely irritating barrier to communication. This can simultaneously embarrass and alienate people alongside ensuring that any information you provide is either misunderstood or ignored. If you are to use jargon that includes acronyms and slang, you need to be absolutely certain that the people you are talking to understands what you are saying. If there is any doubt, leave it out! This is not the time or place to try and impress people with your encyclopaedic knowledge of jargon.

Who delivers the message?

Choosing the right person to deliver your message is very important; this may not be the health and safety leader

You may have heard the expression 'Don't shoot the messenger' where an unfortunate person was held to blame for bad news simply because they had to deliver it! Well, it works the other way too, for information to be received and acted upon correctly, it should be delivered using a credible source, because the messenger delivering the information may be as significant as the information itself. We must ensure the 'right' person for the right audience. This may not be you, it may require that you find someone who you know is trusted by the particular audience you need to engage with. It may be that several people will need to be briefed and they in turn will convey the vital information to specific groups using the appropriate language and communication techniques. This could range from a senior manager to a local worker representative addressing a team, or it could be a health professional eg, an OH nurse or a respected peer. It may require that some training is given to the 'messengers' specifically around the information concerned. It is important that the information is tailored for each audience.

Making it memorable/fun

If you ever wonder why you remember some messages much more than others, irrespective of how important they might be, it could be something to do with the way the message was delivered. When communication is relevant, worthwhile and to the point, it becomes compelling and provokes a (positive) response. Just because a piece of information is important does not mean it cannot be delivered in an engaging or entertaining way. The task is to get people to remember what you need them to remember. How you do it should be based on the audience you are attempting to engage with, their attitudes and behaviour, the type of media they are used to, their attention span, the complexity of the information and how you want them to respond.

A useful device that can be used here is called PASS.

Purpose	What is the information meant to do?
Audience	Who are the audience?
Structure	How will the information be structured (what type of delivery method will be used?
Style	What is the appropriate style for this audience (formal, informal, chatty or official)?

Presenting the same information in different ways

You may have to present the same information in different ways to ensure that each target audience gets the message the way it was intended. For example, people who regularly use social networks or visit YouTube to help solve problems or obtain information, probably will not respond well to printed notes or a formal style report. Those people who read and respond to formal reports and specifications will be more comfortable with this style of communication.

Tailoring the information

Not only should you consider presenting information in different formats but you should also think about tailoring the information to the audience. This will ensure that people will receive information that is relevant to them. The intended audience will be more likely to receive and understand the information. For example, there is no point sending an 'all workers' email (which might include functions like finance and packing sections, for example) containing instructions on a new maintenance strategy that has been implemented. If these types of communication become commonplace workers may start ignoring them as a matter of course as they will make the assumption that there is nothing relevant in it for them. This could, obviously, have a major impact for any industry but especially in the high hazard industries.

How to gather information

A good health and safety leader must ensure that they have gathered the right information before making any conclusions or decisions about situations. We will now look at three tools that may help you in this respect.

The right questions to ask about work activities and when to ask them

Asking the right questions

As we discussed earlier it is really important that you not only ask questions of your workforce, but also that the question is the right question. We have also mentioned earlier that 'open' questions are usually better to ask than closed questions. Open questions require a response other than 'yes' or 'no' and, therefore, let the worker elaborate on their answers. However, there are times were mixed questioning is appropriate. 'Closed' questions are appropriate when you are confirming a piece of information given to you eg, 'You are confirming that there were no reported faults when the equipment was started up?' to which the respondent would answer 'Yes'.

Good health and safety leaders will want to understand why things are done in a particular way. You should not be assuming that because it has always been done that way that this is the only way to work. So, for example, a good question to ask you workforce could be 'what other way could you could carry out that activity that may make it safer for you?' or 'what other equipment would help you to carry out the activity more efficiently but safely at the same time?' and the list goes on. The best time to be asking these questions is during your leadership walkabouts (as discussed earlier). It may be advisable to have a list of questions with you to use as prompts with you when you are on your walkabouts.

However, do not discount other tools such as worker surveys, toolbox talks etc. The workforce may have strong/good ideas but may be too shy to approach you during a normal working day. Workers may prefer to come forward with their ideas during discussions with peers or as part of a survey, especially an anonymous survey.

Active listening

Active listening can be one of the most important tools that a health and safety leader can have. Active listening will enable you to:

- successfully gather information. Leaders should be able to absorb, understand, and consider ideas and points of view from other people without interruption or argument; and
- listen to criticism without reacting defensively.

Good health and safety leaders need to learn to listen first and speak second so that meaningful, balanced communication always takes place. People have two ears but one mouth... what does this tell you?

Active listening is not the same as hearing. Hearing is about being aware of sounds. Listening requires action, you need to concentrate so that you process and understand the meaning of the message and can respond accordingly.

This is often represented using four stages: hearing, attending, understanding and remembering.

Hearing is simply being aware of a sound.

Attending is the act of filtering and screening, so you actually pay attention to the message. This is particularly important (and difficult) if you have issues with the person delivering the message. We need to listen through our prejudices and focus on the message not the messenger.

Understanding means we comprehend what is being said and decode the information we are being given. You should not just switch off until it is time for you to speak again. Listening properly is the only way we can really understand what people need, or what they think about a particular issue or idea.

Remembering means committing information to memory, an essential requirement for active listening. It is also the only way to ensure continuity and the important act of building rapport and a relationship. People like to be remembered and what they say is often important. It is not always easy to do, so make notes if needed. There is little point in a conversation, the sending and receiving of information through a communication channel, if the content of this exchange is instantly lost.

It is worth a mention at this point that the structure of your MBWA activity will involve both giving and receiving information if it is to have value.

Encouraging improvement, innovation and learning (health and safety leadership value 5)

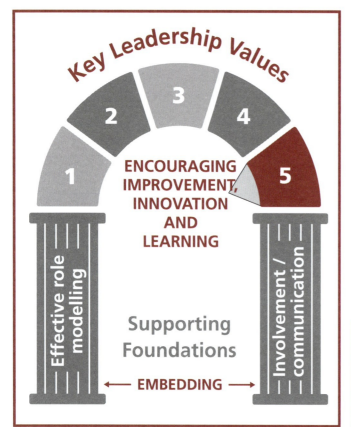

Leaders need to be continually learning from their activities and behaviours

It is important to ensure that development opportunities exist for all those who seek to learn. Professional development has proven to be a powerful motivation tool within many organisations. It also provides a platform for ideas for improvement and innovation to be proposed.

ASSESSMENT ACTIVITY 5

Please refer to the document Unit HSL1, guidance and information for candidates and internal assessors.

*You should now complete task **L5: Encouraging improvement, innovation and learning***

A 'learning organisation' is an organisation that listens, this means that any health and safety leader must also listen if improvement and innovation are to become truly embedded in the culture. Improvement and innovation can come from anywhere, the only way an organisation can learn about it is by ensuring everybody has a voice and that everybody is listened to. Feedback is as important as listening; workers are less likely to want to communicate if they get little or no feedback. An effective leader will know this and be creative in finding ways to develop a continuous process of encouraging innovation and improvement throughout all areas of the organisation. 'Managing by walking about' is one powerful method of gathering information across all levels.

Positive reinforcement, negative reinforcement and punishment

> **KEY TERM**
>
> *Reinforcement*
>
> Reinforcement occurs when a consequence that follows a behaviour makes it more likely that the behaviour will occur again in the future.

Negative and positive reinforcement

As we can see from the 'Key Term' the consequences of our behaviours is a driver for whether that action will happen again.

Negative reinforcement is avoiding a negative outcome or avoiding something that you do not want.

For example, if a worker knows that they will avoid a reprimand because their manager will walk past and not challenge them if they are not following procedures, then the act of walking past will negatively reinforce that unsafe behaviour. They are avoiding a reprimand and are likely to engage in the same behaviour again.

This is why the culture of the organisation is so important; the wrong culture can negatively reinforce the wrong behaviours.

Both positive and negative reinforcement will increase the chance that a behaviour will happen again.

Positive reinforcement is a technique that a good health and safety leader should be adopting to its fullest extent. You need to be reinforcing positive behaviours (in this context, safe acts) so that they will happen again in the future. The best way to achieve this result is by praise. Everybody likes to receive praise, it makes us feel good; a simple 'thank you' can have a massive effect on a worker's day. So, for example, if you see a worker referring to a safe system of work before starting up a machine, you should highlight this by making a point of thanking the worker for following the procedures. This will not only make the worker feel good but will have a bearing on their future behaviours. The worker will recognise the praise and will want to receive this in the future. The worker will want to repeat that action in the future, even when the boss is not around! Not only will the positive reinforcement have a direct effect on the worker in question but it may also have an effect on other workers who may be in the area. They will have seen the worker receiving praise so will want the same for themselves. So you can see that a simple 'thank you' could drive an improvement in safe behaviours throughout the workforce.

It is important for health and safety leaders to acknowledge that their workers will respond to a 'reinforcer'. This can be anything that is added to encourage the behaviour in the future. We have already talked about praise and saying 'thank you' but other reinforcers could include peer approval/disapproval, recognition in organisational newsletters etc or money (a very big reinforcer for many people). You can identify your workers reinforcers through observation and by trialling potential reinforcers. For example, if everyone wears the correct defect-free personal protective equipment for the week, the workforce will be allowed to leave an hour early at the end of the week.

You should also be aware that a reinforcer could be good for one person or bad for another. For example, a manager, who is a vintage car enthusiast, wanted to thank his team for their safe working behaviours. The manager, therefore, arranges for the team to visit a vintage car show. The manager and car enthusiasts in the team have a really good time and will find this a good motivator for the future. However, the rest of the team have no interest in this subject and, therefore, feel the day was a tedious waste of time. This will not motivate the second half of the team to go that extra mile in the future.

We all too often only pick up on something when it goes wrong. However, the opposite is also very important; acknowledgment of safe behaviours should be at the front of health and safety leader's mind, especially when they are undertaking walkabouts or interacting with the workforce in some other way.

Punishment

> **KEY TERM**
>
> *Punishment*
>
>
>
> Involves an individual or group of workers receiving something they do not want (eg, a verbal warning from a supervisor) and/or losing something that they have or would like to have (eg, removal of bonus payments).

Punishment should only be used as a last resort but is appropriate for some situations. As we discussed under blame and just culture, punishment should always been consistent for the offence committed and be the same for all workers no matter what level they are in the organisation. For example, if a finance director refuses to wear personal protective equipment, they should receive the same punishment as a machine operator who has committed the same offence.

We all know that errors will always happen as we are only human. It is, therefore, important that the punishment is proportionate to the offence committed. It is essential that a full root cause analysis is carried out. This will determine the reasons for any errors or violations and the need to understand the local context of the individual at the sharp end of the failure.

Often errors and violations can be traced back to organisational failings eg, management decisions, time pressures, resourcing issues, lack of correct equipment, lack of suitable training etc. We should not be punishing individual workers for errors or violations that are attributable to organisational failings.

There are obviously a whole range of punishments available that a health and safety leader should be aware of. In reality, it is unlikely that the health and safety leader will implement the punishment, but you may, however, be consulted on the type of punishment likely to be given by your organisation's human resources department. It is important to bear in mind the longer time effects any punishment could have on the worker. The worker is very likely already feeling guilty about the incident, especially if the incident has caused pain or longer term injuries to a colleague. You should be using judgement of what you know about the worker in question and the activity being undertaken. For example, if you know that a worker forgot to follow part of a procedure for machinery start-up due to arriving late at work after a sleepless night caused by a newborn baby, but has always diligently followed the rules in the past, you should be advocating for the worker for a lesser, or indeed, no punishment at all. However, if the worker is always ignoring procedures to cut corners to save time, you should be advising human resources of this so that an appropriate punishment can be given.

In addition to internal actions being taken against a worker, there could also be legal ramifications. An individual eg, director, or a worker at any level, can be prosecuted in the UK for offences that breach health and safety legislation (we discussed this earlier in the book).

The following table provides a summary of the main points we have just discussed.

Positive reinforcement	Negative reinforcement	Punishment
Praise from health and safety leader	Avoid peer disapproval	Disciplinary action
Recognition from line manager	Avoid penalties	Removal of rewards
Approval of peers	Actions carried out are to avoid adverse consequences only	Suspension or dismissal

Element 3 **Leadership**

Element 3 references / further reading

References

1 A review of the literature on effective leadership behaviours for safety, Health and Safety Executive, Research Report 952
http://www.hse.gov.uk/research/rrpdf/rr952.pdf

2 Health and Human Potential Website
https://www.ihhp.com/meaning-of-emotional-intelligence

3 Safe Deal cards, Health and Safety Laboratory
https://www.hsl.gov.uk/hsl-shop/safe-deal#product

Further reading

Health and Safety Executive case study
http://www.hse.gov.uk/involvement/casestudies/bardsley.pdf

Leadership and worker involvement toolkit, Good health and safety leadership
http://www.hse.gov.uk/construction/lwit/assets/downloads/good-health-safety-leadership.pdf

Strategies to promote safe behaviour as part of a health and safety management system, HSE, contract research report 430/2002
http://www.hse.gov.uk/research/crr_pdf/2002/crr02430.pdf

Behavioural based safety guide, Health and Safety Authority, Ireland
http://www.hsa.ie/eng/Publications_and_Forms/Publications/Safety_and_Health_Management/behaviour_based_safety_guide.pdf

Notes

Notes

Notes

Notes

Notes